IA

Industrial Archaeology

A SERIES EDITED BY
L. T. C. ROLT

13
The Stationary
Steam Engine

The Industrial Archaeology
of the
Stationary Steam Engine

R. A. Buchanan and George Watkins

Allen Lane

In Memoriam
L. T. C. ROLT
1910-74

with affection and gratitude

Contents

List of Plates

All of the engines illustrated are either actually preserved or due to be preserved, and many of the illustrations were taken when they were performing their regular duty. The plates have been chosen to indicate divergences in designs for similar services, and to show how different designers and engineers varied in their approach to the solution of a specific problem. The notes upon the engines are intended to suggest lines of study that the industrial archaeologist might follow in approaching the steam engine from preserved examples, and they are therefore grouped according to their service as far as possible. All the photographs were taken by George Watkins with the exception of no. 13, which was taken by John Butt.

List of Line Drawings

Preface

This book marks the fruition of almost a decade of happy collaboration between the authors in the Centre for the Study of the History of Technology at the University of Bath. The Centre was founded in 1964, at what was then the Bristol College of Science and Technology, with Angus Buchanan as its Director, and George Watkins was recruited shortly afterwards as a special sort of research assistant. The special nature of the appointment is indicated by the fact that Mr Watkins was already approaching retiring age when he was given this encouragement to organize and complete his unique photographic record of the stationary steam engine which, as the Watkins Collection, is now an indispensable archive on the history of steam technology.

The Centre has pursued three main research interests over the past ten years. These have been: the social impact of technological innovation; industrial archaeology, both local and national; and the task of recording the stationary steam engine. In producing this book we have been able to combine these interests, so that the project represents a professional as well as a personal partnership.

Many people have assisted us in this project, both directly and indirectly, and it is not possible to thank them all by name. Nevertheless, there are several persons and institutions to whom we would like to say a special word of thanks. First, we are grateful to the late Mr L. T. C. Rolt, who persuaded us to undertake the task and refrained from harrying us when we got behind schedule. Tom Rolt was a founder-member of the Advisory Council of the Centre for the Study of the History of Technology, and was always a generous friend in our activities. We are grateful, likewise, to the University of Bath for its encouragement of our work, and in particular we would like to mention those colleagues who have been of immediate help in this project: Mr Keith A. Falconer, Survey Officer to the Council for British

Archaeology, who is based with us at the Centre; Mr Owen Ward, for his consideration and advice on many occasions; Mr John Carpenter, who spent a year with us on a Nuffield Small Grant, mounting the photographs and annotations in the Watkins Collection; Mrs Judith Burchell, who has helped mightily on the secretarial side; and Mr Martin Doughty who, although arriving late on the scene, performed a monumental labour for us in classifying the material in the Watkins Collection and thus making it possible to prepare the Gazetteer.

Amongst our many friends and helpers further afield we would like to thank Mr Frank Wightman for his help with the line drawings; the innumerable Librarians and Museum Curators who have responded patiently and helpfully to our inquiries; and the equally large number of industrial managers, engine-men, and craftsmen who have been obliging and hospitable when we have approached them for information about their steam engines. Our investigations have convinced us that there is a great fund of good-will in Britain for the sympathetic treatment of the surviving stationary steam engines, and we hope that this project will help towards directing this good-will into creative activity.

G. W.

R. A. B.

Note of Abbreviations

Where it has seemed appropriate in the text, and in the list of individual engine specifications in the Gazetteer, we have used certain standard abbreviations in the interest of brevity. For anybody not familiar with them, they are as follows:

rpm: revolutions per minute
psi: pounds per square inch
spm: strokes per minute
hp: horse power

Wherever possible we have given engine specifications in the following order: cylinder bore in inches – cylinder stroke in feet and inches – revolutions per minute or strokes per minute (whichever is applicable) – pounds per square inch of normal boiler operating pressure – horse power.

PART ONE

The Steam Engine in History

CHAPTER ONE

Origins and Early Development

The steam engine is a crucial feature in the study of industrial archaeology. Its invention has been fairly described as one of the outstanding triumphs of human ingenuity, 'comparable in importance with Gutenberg's printing press and the weight-driven clock'.[1] It was, moreover, invented and developed in Britain in its early stages, and it played a significant part in the accelerating process of industrialization which we know as the Industrial Revolution. These facts alone would make the steam engine a machine of extraordinary interest to industrial archaeologists, but its quality has been further enhanced by its obsolescence. In the twentieth century the traditional reciprocating steam engine has been steadily replaced in its locomotive, marine and industrial power forms by other prime movers. Admittedly, steam turbines are still used extensively in large ships and in the process of generating electrical energy, but as a source of power for industrial machinery and transport steam has been effectively replaced by electricity and the internal combustion engine.

One consequence of this is that thousands of steam engines have been taken out of commission and destroyed. Very few still remain at work, and most of those which survive intact are in danger through neglect, impatience to re-develop sites, or the pressing needs of industrial growth and urban renewal. The steam locomotive has disappeared from the standard gauge track of British Rail, although enthusiastic bodies of private citizens are demonstrating up and down the country that such locomotion retains a tremendous appeal as a tourist attraction. Meanwhile, those large stationary steam engines which have fortunately survived their working lives in industry, mining, and the public services, urgently require sympathetic attention in recording and preserving. No subject so well epitomizes the study of industrial archaeology as the steam engine, in its importance, its urgency arising from obsolescence and disappearance, and in the

grandeur and functional elegance of the machines. No subject
more richly deserves a systematic assessment of its contribution
to industrial archaeology.

In attempting to make such an assessment we are obliged to
set clear limits to the exercise in order to make a useful survey
within the scope of a single slim volume. Other volumes in this
series have dealt with railway engineering,[2] so that we feel
justified in excluding the locomotive steam engine except for
occasional references for purposes of comparison with the
development of stationary steam power. We also intend to exclude
any detailed consideration of the steam turbine, as that is far
from becoming obsolete and is thus outside the proper area of
industrial archaeology. Our attention will be concentrated on the
stationary steam engine as a source of power for all manner of
industries and services, from its emergence in a viable form for
pumping water out of deep mines at the beginning of the eighteenth century to its decline and supersession by other sources of
power in the present century. We will seek first to present this
development in its social and industrial context, in order to
understand the role of the stationary steam engine in the British
Industrial Revolution and its repercussions elsewhere. Then, in
the second part of our text, we will examine in some detail the
technical aspects of the steam engine, bearing in mind the need
to make a complex piece of machinery intelligible to industrial
archaeologists who may have little engineering experience.
Finally, we try to provide by way of an extended gazetteer in
Part III a comprehensive survey of the surviving steam engines
in Britain so that industrial archaeologists may know not only
what to look for, but also where to start looking in order to see
for themselves these superb machines now mainly still and silent,
which are all that remain of an enormous number of steam
engines that turned the wheels of British industry for the greater
part of two centuries. We cannot re-create in cold print the
evocative smell of steam and oil or the impressively quiet throb
of a moving steam engine, but we hope that by helping others to
understand the significance of the steam engine we can persuade
them to take advantage of such opportunities as still remain to
enjoy these experiences.

Although the effective history of the steam engine begins,
as we have said, in the eighteenth century, it had a long pre-
history. Ingenious experimenters of the later Hellenic period

such as Hero of Alexandria projected steam reaction turbines although they seem to have applied them to little more than toys, and their work thus has curiosity value rather than significance. Not until the Scientific Revolution which came to fruition with the work of Bacon, Galileo and Newton in the seventeenth century were the principles fundamental to steam power first systematically explored. With Galileo's perception that the action of any machine can be understood as that of one or more levers, and the discovery – remarkable because it was so unexpected – that the atmosphere exerts a uniform pressure on everything at sea-level, the possibility emerged of harnessing air pressure to some sort of mechanical apparatus. Robert Boyle's study of the expansion of gases and the work of von Guericke on the effects of a vacuum carried the process considerably further in the second half of the seventeenth century. The experiments by von Guericke, published in 1672, were particularly significant, because by managing to make an air pump he was able to create a partial vacuum and thus to demonstrate mechanically the pressure of the atmosphere.[3] His apparatus included what was essentially a piston moving in a vertical cylinder. The problem remained of creating a vacuum under the piston in such a way that it could be made to do useful work under the pressure of the atmosphere, and after unsuccessful attempts with gunpowder Denis Papin suggested in 1691 the solution which was eventually to be successful by boiling water in the cylinder and then allowing the steam to condense and thus form a partial vacuum. This sprang from Papin's research on steam and the principle of pressure cookers, but he did not develop it into an engine capable of repeating its stroke several times a minute.

It is not unreasonable to see all this pioneer work as deriving from the ferment of intellectual activity known conveniently as the Scientific Revolution. It was certainly an international movement, with Italian, German and French scientists taking the leading part, but with British scientists, organized since 1662 in the Royal Society, beginning to take an active part, although the major British contribution in this period was undoubtedly the new overall conception of the universe provided by Isaac Newton. One way and another, by the end of the seventeenth century the minimum scientific knowledge essential for the creation of a viable steam engine had been achieved and the remaining problem was a technological one –

namely, how to build an engine which would work usefully. The success of any technological innovation depends upon a delicate combination of social needs and social resources within an environment which is receptive to new ideas, and it is a matter of prime importance in the evolution of the steam engine that, at the time when it became a theoretical possibility, this combination of elements occurred in Britain and not elsewhere.

Britain possessed, after the Glorious Revolution of 1688, a social structure which was flexible and dynamic compared with that of its main European rivals (except Holland – handicapped in other ways), which meant that there were powerful commercial and industrial groups with a progressive philosophy founded on the mechanistic science of Newton and the similarly mechanistic politics of John Locke, who were able and anxious to exploit new ideas. The same powerful social groups were conscious of pressing social needs in the shape of a shortage of fuel which could only be overcome by converting charcoal processes, especially in the iron industry, to coal and by extracting more coal from the abundant supplies which lay buried in many parts of the country. To meet the rapidly expanding demand for coal for both industrial and domestic consumption, however, it was necessary to overcome the severe operating difficulties which restricted the extraction of coal from deep mines, and foremost amongst these problems was the need for an efficient pumping engine. Man power, animal power, and water power had all been harnessed to do this, but none of them provided the reliability and efficiency promised by the steam engine. When this social need was matched by the social resources of capital, materials and skilled mechanics capable of turning their hands to ingenious improvisation, it was only a matter of time before the technical problem of converting a scientific possibility into a piece of useful hardware would be solved, and solved in Britain.

In the event, the first solution was really a false start. After several earlier attempts to raise water by steam power, associated with the Marquis of Worcester and others in the second half of the seventeenth century, none of which appear to have been successful, Captain Thomas Savery took out his famous patent (No. 356 in the Patent Rolls), dated 25 July 1698, for a

new Invention for Raising of Water and occasioning Motion to all Sorts of Mill Work by the Impellent Force of Fire, which will be of great use and Advantage for Drayning Mines, Serveing Towns with Water, and for the Working of all Sorts of Mills where they have not the Benefitt of Water nor constant Windes.[4]

In a publication of 1702, Savery described his invention as 'The Miner's Friend', and despite the wide scope of the patent preamble he had no doubt about the most important potential market for his idea: it was intended to permit the hard-pressed miners of Cornwall and Tyneside to clear their mines of water. It seems likely that Savery's title of 'Captain' derived from his promotion of mining ventures in Cornwall, and it was certain that he was very familiar with the problems of deep tin mining, but a pumping engine using coal as a fuel was even more appropriate in the developing coalfields of the North-East and elsewhere. Unfortunately, it is most unlikely that Savery's device worked satisfactorily in a coal mine or any other sort of mine, because there is little evidence of one ever having been installed for such a use.[5] The reason for this was the existence of intrinsic weaknesses in the design of the steam pump.

Savery's invention was not strictly a machine or engine, as it had no moving parts except valves. In its fully developed form it consisted of a pair of vessels into which steam was admitted alternately. By condensing the steam in each vessel in turn a partial vacuum was created so that atmospheric pressure forced water into first one and then the other. The water was prevented from returning down the inlet pipe by a one-way valve, and as it was expelled from the vessel by the injection of fresh steam it was forced into the upwards pipe through another non-return valve. The apparatus had three formidable working difficulties. In the first place, the use of steam to expel cold water from the vessels was extremely wasteful of heat. Second, the process required the production of steam at a pressure higher than any which could be safely maintained in the boilers available at the time. And thirdly, by depending on atmospheric pressure to raise the water into the vessels, an operating limit of 32 feet was set to this part of the apparatus as this is the maximum height to which a column of water can be raised by the weight of the atmosphere at sea-level. Thus it was not possible to compensate to any great degree for comparatively low boiler pressures by increasing the atmospheric part of the Savery cycle, and the maximum combined effect of suction and pressure was about 50 feet, which made it of little use in a deep mine. In theory, it was possible to overcome this disadvantage by installing a series of Savery pumps in a shaft at 50-feet intervals, but there is no record of this ever having been done, even on an experimental scale. What we do know is that Savery was an astute business-man who was able to exploit his patent in order to secure a share in the development of Newcomen's very different invention, so that some early Newcomen engines were occasionally attributed to Savery for the confusion of posterity. We also know that the Savery apparatus was used, even if not in deep mines, as a short-lift pump raising water to a reservoir for water supply or in order to run it over a water wheel and thus yield rotary action. In this form only the suction part of the Savery cycle was employed. Careful research has produced evidence of several such arrange-ments in the Manchester area still operating late in the eighteenth century,[6] and Rees's *Cyclopaedia* describes one installed in a London coach axle-tree factory by a Mr Keir to drive a water wheel of 18 feet diameter.[7] None survive, so far as we can establish, as industrial archaeological specimens.

Savery's invention marks the transition from the pre-history of the steam engine to the real history. Despite its severe limi-tations, the success of Savery in establishing his patent rights (Parliament in 1699 extended the grant of the patent to 1733, so that even after Savery's death in 1715 a syndicate of London speculators was able to extract royalties on almost every steam engine constructed) and in publicizing the idea of using 'the Impellent Force of Fire' shows clearly the convergence of social needs and social resources within a society which was responsive to innovations if they promised to be profitable. This was the environment in which Thomas Newcomen produced the machine which was to be the first genuine steam engine, even though it made its active stroke under atmospheric pressure and even though the practice of referring to it as a 'fire engine' remained normal until the end of the eighteenth century. Newcomen (1663–1729) was a blacksmith and ironmonger whose home was at Dartmouth in Devon. All attempts at writing his biography have failed to overcome the difficulties presented by sheer lack of information about Newcomen's life, so that he remains a shadowy and problematical figure.[8] The biggest problem has been that of how a man of such humble rank in society could have made an invention incorporating some of the most advanced scientific principles of his day, and this has puzzled commentators in his own time and ever since. But the problem has probably been exaggerated. When it is remembered that Newcomen was literate (at least two letters from him to his wife survive) and that he was a Dissenter belonging to one of those seminal groups in the British Industrial Revolution who made an outstanding contribution because they were excluded from participating in political activity and because they devoted themselves to self-improvement by creating wealth, it becomes entirely credible that Newcomen should have been aware of scientific advances and anxious to improve upon them. The fact that the environment of early eighteenth-century Britain was congenial to a man such as Newcomen does not imply that every hard-working nonconformist blacksmith had a chance of achieving immortality. But it does mean that a humble origin was not an insuperable barrier to a man of genius doing so.

That Newcomen was a genius there can be no doubt, whatever help he received from friends and assistants such as John Calley (a Dartmouth plumber and glazier, and an even more shadowy figure than Newcomen), or from businessmen such as Captain Savery. He took the idea of a piston moving in a vertical cylinder under the pressure of the atmosphere when a vacuum had been created beneath it, combined it with a method of creating a vacuum by condensing steam with a jet of cold water in the cylinder, and controlled this process by a cycle of trigger-mechanisms operating the various valves. He then linked the reciprocating piston with the pumping rods in a mine shaft through a rocking beam arranged in such a way that the downward stroke of the piston overcame the weight of the pumping machinery and its load. At the end of the power stroke, the weight of the pump rods was sufficient to return the piston to its starting position at the top of the cylinder. Steam was provided at little more than atmospheric pressure from a simple boiler which was really only a glorified kettle placed immediately below the cylinder. Newcomen was probably working on this machine for a decade before 1712, gradually improving its efficiency and ironing out its problems. One of his ingenious improvements was that of replacing the manual operation of valves in the early models by an automatic device whereby the valves were triggered by a rod connected to the main beam, with each valve counterbalanced

to give a quick cut-off and opening action which could not be performed by the slow-moving beam. The valves controlled the in-
take of steam, the injection of a spray of water to condense the
steam, and the 'snifting valve' to exhaust the condensate and the
air introduced into the cylinder with the steam. We know little
about these years of experiment, for the first Newcomen engine
of which we have documentary evidence including a detailed
drawing was the fully fledged machine erected at Dudley Castle
in Staffordshire in 1712. The precise site of this engine has been
the subject of controversy, but it seems now to have been settled
beyond reasonable doubt although no trace of the engine or its
house remains.[9]

By 1712 Captain Savery had succeeded in maintaining his
patent rights to license all sorts of fire-engine, thus compelling
Newcomen to work in partnership with him. The result was a
partial eclipse of Newcomen's role in the enterprise, although
posterity has been more kind to him. Indeed, the mid-eighteenth-
century lecturer on scientific subjects, Dr Desaguliers, had already
recognized him as the main author of the steam engine, and by
that time the engine had become widely used.[10] Our knowledge
of the spread of Newcomen-type steam engines is still far from
complete, but enough research has been done to establish the
general pattern. Like the first engine at Dudley, most of the
early engines appear to have been used in coal mines. This was
natural enough, as it was coal mining which presented the most
urgent need for an efficient pumping engine, and the fact that
the engine was heavy on coal consumption was a disincentive to
its use except where coal was cheap. The need for better coal-
mine pumps was particularly acute in the North-East coalfield,
which was by far the most developed coalfield in the country in
the eighteenth century because of its links with the London
market. A reasonably reliable list compiled at the request of
John Smeaton in 1769 registered a total of 98 engines erected
by this date in the North of England and Scotland, the great
majority being in the North-East coalfield. Of these 98, it was
stated that 57 were at work in 1769.[11] By this time there is
evidence of their use in many other coal-mining areas, although
it is doubtful whether any other clusters were as dense as that
of the North-East.[12] Other mining industries such as the metallic
mines of Cornwall and Devon installed several engines, although
the high cost of fuel remained a considerable discouragement in

these areas until Watt's improvements in efficiency in the last quarter of the eighteenth century. Yet other industries built Newcomen engines to provide a water supply for their water wheels, as at the large brass works established at Warmley near Bristol by William Champion.[13] Also, the value of the Newcomen engine as a water-raising pump for public waterworks was quickly recognized, one of the earliest installations being that at York Buildings, near the Strand, in 1726. Although mechanically very successful, this engine was taken out of use after five years because of the high cost of the fuel consumed by it.[14]

The York Buildings engine attracted a lot of attention from visitors, who came to marvel at its power, and throughout the country the spreading popularity of the Newcomen machine generated much interest and, on the part of lay people, much puzzlement to explain its action. Several fascinating attempts to describe Newcomen engines survive from this period. That of the Reverend James Clegg, a nonconformist minister visiting a lead mine in Derbyshire, is typical:

> . . . Saw 3 curious Engines at work there, which by ye force of fire heating water to vapour a prodigious weight of water was raised from a very great depth, and a vast quantity of lead ore laid dry. The hott vapour ascends from an iron pan, close covered, through a brass cylinder fixed to the top, and by its expanding force raised one end of the engine, which is brought down again by the sudden introduction of a dash of cold water into ye same cylinder which condenseth the vapour. Thus the hott vapour and cold water act by turns, and give ye clearest demonstration of ye mighty elastic force of air . . .[15]

All that has been said about the particular appropriateness of the steam engine to the developing industrial needs and resources of Britain in the eighteenth century does not mean that it was inappropriate elsewhere. In fact, considerable interest was shown in Newcomen-type engines on the continent from an early date. In 1726, the same year that the waterworks engine was installed in York Buildings, France acquired its first Newcomen engine at Passy, close to Paris, for pumping from the Seine into the city water supply. Probably somewhat earlier, engines had been erected in Hungary, at Königsberg, and in Austria, at Vienna and Cassel. Martin Triewald, who had known Newcomen personally, returned to his native Sweden to erect the first

steam engine there in 1727. Many of the central European engines seem to have been the work of Isaac Potter, an itinerant
millwright who may have been related to the Potter family in
the Midlands who, being fellow Baptists, had befriended Newcomen when he was looking for markets in their region. On the
whole, however, the enterprise to exploit the new prime mover
was deficient on the Continent, particularly as many European
states had a more extensive and refined waterpower technology
than Britain at that time.[16]

The Hornblower family, another group of Bromsgrove Baptists
which established early links with Newcomen, became famous
engine-builders in Cornwall and elsewhere. In the 1750s they
pioneered the introduction of steam power to the New World
when Josiah Hornblower went out to erect an engine for Colonel
John Schuyler at his copper mine in New Jersey. It took him from
1753 to 1755 to construct the engine, which then worked well
for many years, being twice rebuilt. A fragment from one of the
rebuilt machines survives in the Smithsonian Institution. Other
engines followed in America, at waterworks at Philadelphia and
New York. But in the new nation which emerged with the
Declaration of Independence in 1776 steam power was still a
rare novelty, for in that year a young soldier called Isaac Bangs
described with wonder and puzzled astonishment the engine
recently installed at New York waterworks:

> . . . the mystery was, how the machine in the well was first
> actuated and kept in motion. This (as I at length discovered,
> with surprise,) was done by the power of boiling water. I
> found that, by means of a large copper boiler, the steam or
> vapor of the water is conveyed from thence into a strong
> copper tube of 18 inches and 10 feet long, which stands in a
> perpendicular position. The lower part or end of this tube is
> tight, but the upper end has in it a moveable stopper which
> may move upwards or downwards with as much ease as pos-
> sible, and at the same time keep the air without from
> entering into the tube. In order to keep it tight, another part
> of the works constantly supplies the top of the tube, above the
> stopper, with a small jet of water. The stream of the hot
> water (as I take it) entering the tube, rarefies the air therein
> to a great degree, when the stopper is let loose and flies upward
> with rapidity to the upper end of the tube, and immediately is

thrown back by the pressure of the air from without. When it gets to the bottom, it is again driven upwards by the same cause as before, and repelled downward in like manner by the air, causing a constant motion. To this stopper a stout lever is fastened in the middle upon the axis. The lever is moved up and down by the stopper in the tube, and thus works the engine as well . . .[17]

A great virtue of the Newcomen engine was that it was robust and fairly simple, so that once one had been well constructed it could be relied upon to operate effectively with the minimum of maintenance and attention. The early erectors were generally blacksmiths turned millwrights, who would purchase a cylinder from a brassfounder (iron gradually replaced brass as the normal material for the cylinder casting during the eighteenth century) and then build the engine complete with its house on the site where it was required, using local materials and labour as much as possible in order to cut costs to the mininum. The syndicate which acquired the rights on Savery's patent was able to secure royalties on most of the early steam engines, but with the lapse of the patent in 1733 there was no legal restriction to the spread of steam engines, and many improvements in detail were incorporated in the design as experience of operating them increased, although there was remarkably little change in the fundamental pattern as devised by Newcomen until the experiments by James Watt. Even after Watt-type engines had become available, many operators preferred to retain their Newcomen machines because of the substantially higher cost of the more efficient Watt engines. Thus many Newcomen machines remained in operation into the nineteenth century, and a few, such as that of the Ashton Vale Iron Company at Bristol which was dismantled in 1900, and that at Farme colliery near Glasgow which ceased work in 1915,[18] even into the present century. We are fortunate that this capacity for continued use has resulted in the survival of a few Newcomen engines. The Science Museum has one and also a Heslop engine which incorporates an embryonic form of compounding by using the steam twice.[19] More significant as industrial monuments are the engines at Elsecar and Dartmouth. That at Elsecar, near Sheffield, was used for pumping in a coal mine for a hundred years from 1823 to 1923 and remained workable until 1939. It is believed

to have originated in 1787, but underwent numerous modifi-
cations, and now has a cast-iron beam. It has been preserved to
date by the National Coal Board, but has now been scheduled as
an ancient monument. The Dartmouth engine, in a special
engine house near the waterfront in the town of Newcomen's
birth, was re-erected on this site by the initiative of the Newcomen Society in 1964, with the late Mr Arthur Pyne taking the
leading part in moving the engine from beside the Coventry
Canal at Hawkesbury. Like other long-lived Newcomen engines,
this one has been much altered and in its present form includes a
'pickle pot', a vessel beneath the cylinder into which the condensing stream of cold water was injected, a device for circum-
venting the Watt patent. But the untrussed wooden beam and
chain connections suggest an early origin, and it is possible that
parts of this engine go back to very early days of Newcomen engine construction. It makes a worthy memorial to the great
inventor, and is a place of pilgrimage for every industrial
archaeologist.

Contrary to persistent legend, James Watt did not invent the
steam engine, and we do not know whether he was ever inspired
to innovate by watching a kettle simmering on the fire. But it
would be fair to say that while many people have watched a kettle
simmering, it requires imaginative genius of a high order to
perceive in such a simple event the possibility of a great invention; and Watt was certainly a man of genius. The result of
bringing a highly perceptive mind trained in craftsmanship and
instrument-making to bear on the problem of making a model
engine work more efficiently resulted in the series of inventions
by which James Watt, in business partnership with Matthew
Boulton, transformed the steam engine from a rough but robust
piece of hardware, wasteful of fuel and capable of only single
reciprocating actions, into an efficient product of skilled engineering, capable of rotary action and thus applicable to a very wide
range of industrial processes. In a sense this achievement
created the modern engineering industry, because it combined
for the first time the skills of the precision-instrument maker
with those of the millwright to create large machines to a higher
standard of accuracy than ever before. The Boulton & Watt
factory at Soho in Birmingham thus became an important training ground and model for a new engineering industry in which
the steam engine had a most important formative role.

James Watt took out his patent for the separate condenser in 1769, following several years of experiment while employed as instrument maker to the University of Glasgow, including his work on the model Newcomen engine which can still be seen at the University. Many years after the event, Watt described how the idea came to him one Sabbath afternoon as he was walking on the Green of Glasgow in 1765:

> . . . the idea came into my mind, that as steam was an elastic body it would rush into a vacuum, and if a communication was made between the cylinder and an exhausted vessel, it would rush into it, and might be there condensed without cooling the cylinder . . . I had not walked further than the Golf-house when the whole thing was arranged in my mind.[20]

Watt had perceived that the most wasteful feature of the Newcomen-type engine was that it alternately heated and cooled the cylinder on every stroke, and that this dissipation of energy could be avoided by keeping the vessel containing the hot steam (the cylinder) separate from that in which the steam was condensed by bringing it into contact with cold water (the condenser), with an arrangement of valves between the two in order to draw off the steam to the condenser at the right moment in each stroke. The cylinder could then be kept permanently hot, with a jacket to prevent loss of heat, and the condenser permanently cool, with a pump operating off the main engine beam to clear the condensate. The model which Watt made to illustrate this brilliant perception can still be seen at the Science Museum, but it proved to be a difficult task converting the idea into reality. Watt first entered into partnership with John Roebuck of Carron Ironworks, and fragments of the experimental engine which they constructed can still be seen at Kinneil House in West Lothian. But they were frustrated by the problem of getting sufficiently well-machined parts for their engine, and when Roebuck got into financial difficulties his friend Matthew Boulton took the opportunity of offering to take Watt into partnership himself. Thus began the famous partnership of Boulton & Watt which was responsible for turning out some 500 steam engines in the quarter century between 1775 and 1800, the period for which Watt's original patent remained in force.

The qualities brought by Matthew Boulton to the partnership were business acumen and the control, in his Soho factory, of a

team of craftsmen capable of making the finely machined parts
needed for Watt's engines. The partners were fortunate that the
establishment of their enterprise coincided with the patent taken
out by the neighbouring ironfounder, John Wilkinson, for boring
cannon and cylinders with unprecedented precision, and for
several years all their cylinders were prepared by Wilkinson.
Within a few years of setting up in business at Birmingham,
Watt had added several further improvements in the steam
engine to his initial patent for the separate condenser. Amongst
these, the invention of the parallel motion gave Watt particular
satisfaction because of its geometrical elegance: it is a device
of swinging rods to transmit the thrust from the piston to the
beam while maintaining the piston rod in a vertical position,
and it became a standard feature on beam engines. Of more
general significance was Watt's invention of a reliable means of
rotary action, by which the reciprocating action of the piston,
used directly for pumping purposes, could be converted to drive
the wheels of all sorts of industrial processes and – potentially –
a means of locomotion. To do this, he devised the curious 'sun
and planet' gearing because he feared patent trouble if he used a
crank, which had been the subject of a patent by James Pickard
in 1780.[21] It is doubtful whether this patent could have stood
up to challenge, and the crank quickly became the standard form
of transmission on all rotary-action steam engines. But the sun
and planet gearing can still be seen on the Boulton & Watt
engine in the Science Museum. The 'planet' was a cogged wheel
attached to the connecting rod from the end of the beam opposite
the cylinder, and was fixed so that it ran round the circumference
of the similar wheel (the 'sun') on the axle of the flywheel
and driving-shaft, to which it transmitted the stroke from the
piston.

Two other innovations by Watt helped to establish the form
which the steam engine was to enjoy for the next hundred years.
One was the centrifugal governor. The development of rotary
action made necessary careful control of the speed of the engine
to ensure uniform motion and to prevent the risk of the engine
running too quickly. Watt adopted a form of automatic control
which seems to have been already well established in windmills,[22]
but greatly improved it. The Watt governor consisted of two
weights mounted on a rotating spindle driven by the engine: as
the weights moved outwards under centrifugal pressure they

gradually closed a 'butterfly' valve until the engine reached the predetermined equilibrium speed. Finally, Watt made a notable advance in steam-engine technique by developing double-action. His early engines had been single-acting atmospheric engines like those of Newcomen – that is, it was the downward pressure of the atmosphere on the upper face of the piston which performed the power-stroke of the engine, and the return or upwards movement of the piston was a dead stroke induced by the weight of the pump rods or load on the engine. Watt also continued the established pattern of using steam at low pressure, little more than that of the atmosphere, because he feared the danger of boiler explosions if the steam pressure should be increased substantially above air pressure. But by completely enclosing his cylinder in order to keep it permanently hot, Watt had to find a substitute for atmospheric pressure and did so by admitting steam above the piston as the vacuum was created below it. The next step was the realization that with a completely enclosed cylinder the process could be reversed, the vacuum being created *above* the piston while steam was admitted below it. Thus was born the principle of double-action, which gave a much smoother movement to the engine and was specially suitable for rotary motion although it did not dispense with the need for a heavy flywheel to store up the momentum of a reciprocating movement and convert it to uniform rotation. The use of steam to replace the pressure of the atmosphere in double-acting engines was a first step towards using the steam expansively, although only to a very limited extent. Watt recognized the possibility of expansive working, but as the advantage was minimal with low-pressure steam he did not pursue this line of development, which had to await the coming of high-pressure steam.

It has been argued that Watt's jealous protection of his patent rights in the decade before their expiry in 1800 restricted the development of the steam engine, and that his opposition to high-pressure steam and to steam locomotion delayed these important innovations. There is some evidence in support of this thesis, and the innovations certainly came rapidly as soon as Watt's supervision was removed. But this view tends to overlook the tremendous contribution which Watt made to the evolution of the steam engine, and to exaggerate such slight delay as there might have been in working out some of its implications in ways in which

Watt himself was not interested. It can also be maintained that the delays in development caused by the restrictions of the patent may have been an advantage, as constructional techniques improved immensely during that period and contributed largely to the accelerated rate of evolution afterwards.

In any event, James Watt transformed the steam engine from a simple pumping instrument into a sophisticated and versatile prime mover which could be applied to an almost limitless range of industrial processes, and as soon as the possibility of providing such an engine emerged there arose a vociferous demand for it. 'The people of London, Manchester and Birmingham are *steam mill mad*', Boulton wrote to Watt in 1781 when urging him to apply himself to the problem of rotary motion. Watt complained that 'surely the devil of rotations is afoot', but his triumphant solution to this problem kept the order books of the Soho firm full to capacity for the remaining years of the patent, for although not entirely clear of financial difficulties they were never short of work. To produce some 500 engines in twenty-five years was a very considerable achievement of industrial management as well as one of superlative technological competence, especially as virtually every machine was planned from scratch to meet the specifications of the customer and the restrictions of the site where it was to be erected. In the early days the firm purchased cylinders from Wilkinson, but they later acquired a foundry of their own. The working parts were all machined in Birmingham, and then all the pieces were dispatched to the site to be assembled under the supervision of an agent of the firm. It was in this capacity that William Murdock served the firm in Cornwall, erecting dozens of engines in Cornish tin and copper mines while carrying out his own experiments with gas lighting and steam locomotion in his house at Redruth. Once assembled, the engine was handed over to the customer and paid for on the basis of a royalty or 'premium' calculated according to the amount of fuel saved in comparison with a Newcomen engine, the sum being fixed at one third of the value of the fuel saved. To enable this calculation to be made Watt devised the measurement of energy which he named 'horse power' (one unit of which can raise 33,000 lb. one foot high per minute), although of more immediate importance was the task of keeping careful accounts of fuel consumption and of the number of strokes performed by the engine. The firm amassed voluminous paper-work in connection with this method of payment, as well as the correspondence between the partners and their agents and the wonderful set of engine drawings, much of which collection survives in Birmingham City Library.[23]

On the basis of this documentary material it is possible to derive a distribution map of the engines produced up to 1800, although of course it is not possible to allow for the movement of engines subsequent to purchase even though it is certain that such movement frequently occurred. The resulting distribution shows five areas of heavy concentration. Three of these are those mentioned by Boulton in the quotation above – London, Birmingham and Manchester. The London engines were mainly lighter engines of under 40 hp, and were installed in a great variety of industries, including several breweries and those in the pioneering but ill-fated Albion Mill at the Southwark end of Blackfriars Bridge – the first steam-powered corn mill in the world.[24] The Birmingham concentration, covering the Black Country and eastern Shropshire around Coalbrookdale, contained a mixture of light and heavy engines, being again spread over many industries but with a preponderance in the iron industry following the precedent of John Wilkinson who was one of the first customers of the firm and always quick to adopt each innovation in the steam engine. The third concentration, in South Lancashire around Manchester, was dominated by engines for cotton mills. The other two main groups of Boulton & Watt engines were in the North-East coalfield, where they gradually displaced Newcomen engines as the more efficient pumping machines, and in Cornwall, where they drove pumps for the deep tin and copper mines. Cornwall had a particularly high proportion of large engines, above 40 hp. Elsewhere, the new engines were spread thinly. The southern counties, from Devon to Sussex, had hardly any, and the eastern counties and those of north and central Wales were similarly empty. There were a number of heavy engines in the metal-working centres of South Wales and a few in Gloucestershire associated with textile mills, and at least one – the large 53·2 hp engine at Thames Head – on the Thames and Severn Canal. The Midland counties other than the Black Country had a few small groups of engines in the Potteries of Staffordshire, in Derbyshire lead and iron works, and in South Nottinghamshire, while the West Riding of Yorkshire had several with a further half dozen in the East Riding at Hull.

There were also several Boulton and Watt engines in Scotland, and others erected abroad.[25]

The partnership of Boulton & Watt was thus extraordinarily productive and important. They demonstrated that there was a pressing industrial need for a reliable prime mover divorced from the traditional sources of animate and natural energy, and they showed how this need could be met in abundance. They set a pattern, both in the type of low-pressure steam engine which they perfected, and in the service which they offered to industry. They also set a pattern, as we have seen, for the incipient engineering industry, of which the steam engine was to be for long a staple ingredient. These were early days yet in the spread of steam power, and for most industrial processes older and more traditional sources of power were still the general rule. But by revealing the immense possibilities of steam power Boulton & Watt provided a model which was reproduced and expanded in the subsequent century.

CHAPTER TWO

Apotheosis

The Industrial Revolution would have occurred in Britain when it did even without the steam engine, but it is certain that it would have developed more slowly and that its impact would have been slighter unless some alternative prime mover had emerged to meet the mounting demand for industrial power. As no such alternative became available until the second half of the nineteenth century, and as both the theory and practice of the internal combustion engine relied heavily upon experience of steam engines, it seems unlikely that Britain would have achieved its spectacular leadership in the early phases of rapid industrialization without the aid of the steam engine. Although it was only one among several significant factors it is thus not unreasonable to see the steam engine as the instrument whereby Britain became the workshop of the world and the acknowledged political and economic leader in the nineteenth-century concert of nations. We have already seen that the steam engine originated in work performed by an international body of scientists, but its development in the eighteenth century had been almost entirely a British achievement, and it was Britain which took the lead in exploiting the application of the steam engine in the nineteenth century. The steam engine has been the outstanding British contribution to the history of technology. Its effect in showing how the power starvation restricting the growth of industry could be overcome, has been among the most important British contributions to the world community.

At the beginning of the nineteenth century the indications of this future pattern were obscure, to say the least. Europe was locked in an exhausting ideological and military struggle between the forces of France, transformed politically by the French Revolution of 1789 and the following upheaval, and those of the other nations fighting to preserve themselves from the scourges of French militarism and French Jacobinism. Britain, secure in its

island fortress, avoided the former but not the latter, and succes-
sive governments sought to restrict the spread of radical and
democratic tendencies amongst the mass of the population.
Nevertheless, Britain enjoyed a self-confidence and relative prosperity in this conflict which was not shared by either its allies or
its enemies, despite the fact that the other nations, and especially
France, had for long been larger and wealthier than herself. This
confidence was based partly on the command of the seas secured
by Lord Nelson at Trafalgar in 1805, and this victory also marked
the successful culmination for Britain of a closely fought struggle
with France for commercial and mercantile superiority in the
markets of the world. The sense of confidence was based also in
part on the consciousness of a rising population, manifest in the
bustling activity of rapidly growing towns despite the gloomy
prognostications of the Rev. T. R. Malthus, who was forecasting
in 1799 that population would increase more quickly than food
and other resources necessary to sustain it. Even more important
than these factors, however, as a reason for national confidence
was the promise inherent in recent achievements that the problem envisaged by Parson Malthus could be overcome and that a
rising population could be combined with a standard of life which
did not decline and which could, hopefully, eventually be improved. This promise of rising productivity was the first-fruit and
most abiding achievement of the Industrial Revolution. Its fulfil-
ment reinforced the national self-confidence and focused attention
on the economic and social transformation by which it had been
reached, so that other nations tried, with varying measures of
success, to emulate the experience of rapid industrialization.

Fundamental to the success of the Industrial Revolution in
Britain was the achievement of certain key industries in securing
massive increases in productivity. The iron and steel industry did
this over one and a half centuries in which coal replaced charcoal
as the main fuel and processes were perfected for producing cast
iron, wrought iron and steel in large quantities and cheaply. The
food and drink industries achieved a similar end over the same
period by a massive reorganization of British farming and the
introduction of new techniques. The cotton textile industry did
it in a mere eighty years, during which it was transformed from
a scattered and relatively unimportant domestic industry into
a massive, mechanized, factory-organized and urban industry.
Behind all these achievements, and those made simultaneously

in old-established industries like ceramics and glass, and in new industries like heavy chemicals and engineering, there lay another achievement: that of overcoming the shortage of power. Without the steam engine this shortage would have strangled – or at least seriously curtailed – British industrial expansion, for despite all the improvements made in water wheels and windmill design by John Smeaton and other engineers there would not have been sufficient power available from natural sources to meet the rapid growth in demand. As it was, the development of the steam engine coincided precisely with the escalating need for industrial power, and was able to supply this need by a remarkable programme of continuing improvement and refinement which began, as we have seen, in the eighteenth century and which continued throughout the nineteenth century. In this period, then, steam power became one of the essential ingredients in British industrial supremacy.

It must be stressed that development of the steam engine continued throughout the nineteenth century. For all its brilliant innovations and unprecedented efficiency, the Boulton & Watt engine was only a step in this process, and without further improvement it could have met only a fraction of the needs of industry in the decades following the expiry of the patent in 1800. This evolution of the steam engine is important to industrial archaeologists because it suggests a basic typology which helps in the recognition and dating of engines. For this purpose, the Newcomen and Watt machines can be grouped together as 'atmospheric' or 'low-pressure' engines under the general heading of 'early types'. They were all beam engines, being usually built into the structure of their engine houses ('house built'), with all except the later Boulton & Watt models having timber beams, although cast-iron beams were introduced about the turn of the century. Early types continued to be extensively used in the nineteenth century and even underwent some development along lines which were later abandoned. The 'grasshopper engine', with the beam hinged at one end rather than in the centre, and the 'side-lever engine', with the beam carried low along the side of the engine to lower the centre of gravity for marine navigation purposes, were of this type. Early types generally were superseded by other steam engines in the course of the nineteenth century, but some remained in use, and a few specimens survive for inspection in museums.

The next major development in steam power occurred right at the beginning of the century with the introduction of *high-pressure steam*. This step was pioneered by Richard Trevithick, who managed to construct boilers capable of withstanding pressures up to 50 psi, and with these built engines which produced considerably more power in relation to size than the early types. Simultaneously, Oliver Evans was experimenting with high-pressure engines in the United States, where an indigenous engineering industry was already beginning to produce its own distinctive innovations and traditions in steam-engine design. Trevithick quickly saw that the advantages of the high-pressure engine overcame one of the most serious objections – that of bulk – to using the steam engine as a means of locomotion, and his engine of 1804 for the Penydarren tramroad in South Wales counts as the first practical steam locomotive, although he had experimented with a road vehicle in Cornwall before that, and even earlier William Murdock had adapted a conventional engine for locomotive purposes. Trevithick thus stands at the parting of the ways in two senses in the evolution of steam power, as the successful promoter both of high-pressure engines and of the steam locomotive. With the latter, the spectacular history of steam traction, we are only concerned incidentally in this account. But high-pressure steam had a tremendous effect also on steam power for industry, and with this we are very much concerned.

In some ways, the most impressive type of steam engine ever built was the *Cornish engine*. This was 'Cornish' in the senses that it was made in large numbers by Cornish engineering firms, and that it was Cornish skill stemming from Trevithick's exploration of high-steam pressures which was responsible for many of its design features. It is not easy to be precise about the distinctive features of a Cornish engine, but it is a fair approximation to say that it was a type of steam engine combining high-pressure, expansive use of steam, and condensing action in a carefully regulated cycle of events during each stroke. By using steam at high pressure it was possible to harness effectively the expansive energy of the steam on one side of the piston as well as the vacuum produced in the condenser on the other side, and an ingenious arrangement of vertical rods operated 'cut-off' levers on the valves in such a way that enough steam remained in the cylinder at the end of each stroke to cushion the piston and thus to give it a smoother action. This design proved itself well suited to the heavy duties required for pumping in the Cornish metal mines, and the remains of many large ruinous engine houses in the county testify to their value in this industry and create one of the most splendid industrial archaeological landscapes in the world. In most cases only the masonry shells survive to indicate the massive proportions of the engine which they contained, but a few engines have been preserved in Cornwall, mainly by the devotion of a small band of enthusiasts in the Cornish Engines Preservation Society (now the Trevithick Society), and these are well worth a visit. They include two in Camborne: one used for pumping at the East Pool mine, and the other adapted by a connecting rod and crank to a drum for winding (an arrangement known as a 'whim' in Cornwall). Another steam whim has been preserved in its engine house at the Levant Mine, on the cliff tops near Land's End. The importance of these three engines has been recognized by the National Trust, which has taken them into its care. A further Cornish engine has been preserved in the works museum of Holmans, the Camborne engineering firm, along with an interesting collection of models and other equipment. Trevithick's cottage, incidentally, is near the town, and his statue broods over the central square.

Although thickest on the ground in their native county, Cornish engines were built all over the country and, indeed, all over the world. Two fine specimens of Watt engines adapted to the Cornish cycle can still be seen actually at work, on special occasions, in the restored steam pumping station at Crofton on the Kennet and Avon Canal. A superb set of six Cornish engines survived until 1968 in a large engine house at Sudbrook in Monmouthshire, where they had been installed in 1886 to drain the Severn Tunnel, but British Rail had no interest in preserving them and so they were destroyed. Another remarkable group has been more fortunate, one having been preserved by the enlightened policy of the Dutch authorities towards their industrial heritage: it is the magnificent Cruquius Engine in Holland, an eight-beamed Cornish giant with annular cylinders (it had a high-pressure cylinder inside the low-pressure cylinder) built by Harveys of Hayle in 1845 as part of the Haarlemmermeer drainage scheme, near Amsterdam, and retained as the centrepiece of a small museum.[1] Most Cornish engines were not compounded, and when they were, the Cornish cycle strictly speaking only occurred in the low-pressure cylinder. Again, most Cornish engines were beam engines, usually having massive cast-iron beams. A few, however, dispensed with the beam and linked the piston rod directly with the pumping mechanism from the bottom of the cylinder: this is the arrangement of the 'Bull' engine, specimens of which have been saved from the Sudbrook site by the Science Museum and the National Museum of Wales in Cardiff.

From the use of high-pressure steam it was a simple step to that of *compounding* – that is, using the steam more than once, at decreasing pressures, by passing it from one cylinder to another working at a lower pressure. Compounding adds considerably to the economy and power of an engine, so that the practice eventually became widely adopted in new designs; but in the early decades of the nineteenth century there were considerable difficulties in modifying existing beam engines satisfactorily to take advantage of it. This was first achieved in the *Woolf compound* arrangement, in which the high-pressure cylinder was placed alongside the low-pressure cylinder, exhausting the steam directly from the former into the latter. With both cylinders acting together on the same end of the beam, this design placed a great strain on the centre. As a result, it did not prove to be generally attractive for the many heavy-duty Cornish engines built in the first half of the century. The system patented by William Mc-Naught of Glasgow in 1845 and known as *McNaughting* overcame the most serious weakness of the Woolf design by placing the high-pressure cylinder between the beam pivot and the crankshaft, so that its movements were opposite to those of the low-pressure cylinder, and this helped to balance the stresses in the beam and engine mounting. McNaughting was widely adopted, but it proved less effective than it might have done because by the middle of the century the traditional beam-type engine was being replaced in popularity by *horizontal* and *inverted vertical* types. McNaughting was applied to many beam engines, although only a few survive today, and the Woolf system of compounding enjoyed a further lease of life with its application to large water-pumping units. The four beam engines installed as late as 1902 to pump water from a reservoir at Blagdon near Bristol were of this type, and two of these have been preserved by Bristol Water Works.

Compounding could be applied more easily to other types of steam engine than it could to beam engines, which was one factor encouraging the transition from the beam to other designs

in the middle decades of the nineteenth century. Indeed, in retrospect it is difficult to account for the popularity of the cumber-
some beam even after other arrangements had become available,
except perhaps for pumping purposes, where the swinging beam
retained some advantages. There was a certain prejudice against
horizontal cylinders derived from the fear that pressure of the
piston on the lower side would cause it to wear unevenly, and
this belief was shared by the early locomotive engineers, who,
apart from Trevithick with his Penydarren locomotive, equipped
their engines with vertical cylinders until Robert Stephenson
experimented first, in the *Rocket*, with diagonal cylinders, and
immediately afterwards moved a stage further to horizontal
cylinders mounted between the wheels of the locomotives. The
experience of locomotive builders with this arrangement in the
1830s convinced steam engineers that it was both efficient and
convenient, so that horizontal designs became normal for stationary steam engines also in the second half of the century. An early
model was that introduced by Taylor Martineau in 1825, and it
was quickly developed in a wide range of sizes because of the
cheapness of the installation and its considerable flexibility compared with the traditional beam engine. Together with the introduction of high pressure and compounding, this transition from
beam to horizontal arrangements provides one of the major typo-
logical features in the evolution of the steam engine.

The flexibility of horizontal-type engines was demonstrated by
their easy adaptation to compound arrangements. In some cases
a high-pressure horizontal engine was coupled to the same
driving-shaft as a low-pressure beam engine, but most horizontal
compound engines were built with the high- and low-pressure
cylinders one behind the other (*tandem*) or side-by-side (*cross
compound*). By the second half of the nineteenth century triple
and even quadruple expansion engines were being built on these
patterns and generating large horse-powers for a wide range of
industrial applications, although quadruples were generally used
for marine rather than stationary service. In some ways the reciprocating stationary steam engine can be regarded as having
reached the highest peak of its development in the large cotton
textile mills of Lancashire in this period, with high-power engines
mainly of compounded horizontal forms, and usually produced by
local engineers of whom several illustrious firms arose particularly to serve the needs of this industry. The sheer size of these

engines has made it difficult to secure their preservation in a period when the Lancashire cotton industry has been undergoing rapid and drastic reorganization, but a few have been saved by the activities of the Northern Mill Engines Preservation Society, and specimens survive as show-pieces, such as the 450 hp engine preserved outside India Mill, Darwen, and the large 1500 hp engine at Dee Mill, Shaw, near Oldham.

Paradoxically, the *uniflow* engine, which may be regarded as the highest development of the steam engine in terms of thermal efficiency, normally reverted to a simple non-compounding arrangement. In this design the steam is admitted at both ends of the cylinder but exhausted through apertures in the middle so that the steam does not reverse its flow in the cylinder and heat losses are thus greatly reduced. It is also a matter of some paradox and irony that this ultimate thermodynamic refinement in the British steam engine was perfected by Dr Johann Stumpf of Charlottenburg in 1908, and was only manufactured under licence by British firms. When it is remembered that other significant innovations in the steam engine after 1850 – like the drop valve engines as developed by Sulzers in Switzerland[2] and the outstanding engines made by Corliss in America[3] – were being pioneered on the Continent and in the United States, it is clear that the apotheosis of the steam engine was not just a British achievement. The firm of Tosi in Italy was described as the finest steam-engine manufacturer in Europe at the Paris Exhibition of 1900,[4] and by this time some large Yorkshire mills like Mons Mill at Todmorden were purchasing their engines from continental manufacturers such as Carels of Ghent. The trend towards continental designs in Lancashire followed upon reports of high economy with superheated steam, which was quickly adopted by British manufacturers. Even though they did not always lead in steam technology, British engineers readily adopted good practice.

For all its great success, the horizontal steam engine always had to compete with other arrangements. We have already noticed that for some pumping duties Cornish engines and other forms of beam engine were used throughout the operating history of steam power. For marine propulsion, the early *side-lever* design was replaced in the mid-nineteenth century by other patterns. *Oscillating* engines, with the piston rod driving directly onto a crank from a cylinder mounted so that it rocked with the movement of the crank, were used in many early steam ships. Then the *inverted vertical* design came into vogue, because it could be arranged compactly along the keel of a ship with the cylinders set in series from higher to lower pressures and with all the piston rods driving downwards to crankpins on the propeller shaft. Such was the attention given to this form of engine by marine engineers that it became a highly efficient type of steam engine and was adopted for many other purposes in industry and public services. Some striking specimens survive, such as the Lilleshall triple-expansion inverted vertical pumping engine installed by the Bristol Water Works Company at Chelvey.

We have now outlined the main features in the evolution of the stationary steam engine during the nineteenth century, but the variations within these broad categories were legion, depending on the exigencies of site, materials available, and the practices of different engineers. Forms of mounting steam engines also developed greatly, especially when the practice of providing *house-built* engines was abandoned in favour of making free-standing machines which had then to be supplied with very substantial engine-beds in order to withstand the stresses created by a large engine, and, in the case of beam engines, elaborate frames and entablatures to carry the beam and to tie it firmly to its base. The development of free-standing machines was made possible by the use of cast iron in place of the timber used extensively in the beam and mountings of the earlier house-built engines, and the introduction of large castings for this purpose made easier the embellishment by decorative motifs and flutings which became a characteristic feature of cast-iron designs. These trimmings tended to disappear later in the century, as steel progressively replaced cast iron as the major constructional material. This transition is seen most clearly in the design of the connecting rod, which in its cast-iron form was almost invariably cruciform in cross-section, whereas the steel connecting rod which replaced it was smooth-surfaced and slightly bulbous towards the centre in order to resist bending stresses.

The more technical aspects of these design features are considered in Part II of this account, together with a discussion of such important ancillary details as valves, transmission and boilers. At this point nothing more need be said of them other than that they underwent the same pattern of development during the nineteenth century which characterized the steam engine as a whole. Altogether, it was a remarkable success story, with the designers and engineers responding to every demand upon them for greater power and improved efficiency. The threat of power-starvation was triumphantly overcome as Britain equipped itself with a prime mover which could be varied in size from engines of a few horse power for a small workshop to the gargantuan engines which drove cotton mills. The success of the steam engine in its first explicit task, that of Savery's 'Miner's Friend', was such that British coal production rose constantly and dizzily, reaching its all-time peak in 1913, so that the steam engine played a major part in supplying its own fuel. It served the coal-mining industry primarily as a pumping engine, but it also came to be the indispensable source of power in the coal mines, for winding coal and men up the shaft, for driving the ventilating fans, and for powering conveyors and other pithead equipment. The service of the steam engine to metalliferous mining in Cornwall and elsewhere has already been mentioned: it is barely less important than the contribution to the coal industry and it is certainly even more dramatic in its visual remains. In working metals steam engines played a virtually indispensable part in the growth of industries in the nineteenth century, and particularly the iron and steel industry. It is impossible to imagine the construction of the huge mills for forging, rolling and slitting iron and steel, which sprang up in the Black Country, South Yorkshire, South Wales and elsewhere, without the steam engine. In forging, for example, Nasmyth's innovation of the inverted vertical form of steam engine as a steam hammer transformed the scale of work that could be considered as feasible, and it was soon adapted to conventional services. In the same way virtually every industrial process in the country, from the very small to the very large, was made easier and more productive by the application of steam power. The same was true of the public services. When the problems of water supply and sewage disposal were at last seriously tackled by private companies and municipal authorities in the second half of the nineteenth century, the steam engine was available as their invaluable aid, to pump water from wells and reservoirs and to keep the drainage systems in motion. Some of the last surviving steam engines to be in operation are in those services, and many of those which have been preserved are in water or drainage works. Prominent amongst these are the London water-pumping engines still at work at Kempton Park, and the batteries of pumps, now idle but pre-

served, at Crossness and West Ham, near the out-falls of the
Southern and Northern main sewers respectively. Elsewhere,
there are fine specimens at Ryhope in County Durham, Papplewick near Nottingham, and Abbey Lane in Leicester.

With the colossal increases in the production and productivity
of British industry during the nineteenth century, and with the
equally dramatic transformation of British society which accompanied it, it is is not surprising that the intimate relationship
between these processes and the spread of steam technology
in Britain should have received attention from commentators in
all walks of life. It was not always favourable comment, because
however great the general increase in prosperity, it appeared
to many sensitive souls to have been accompanied by a great
deal of avoidable human anguish in the highly disciplined new
factories and the sprawling new towns. Thus Blake's 'sooty
imagery' inveighed against the 'dark Satanic mills' and the
engines which drove them, even though he never went north
of the Trent,[5] and the Romantic Movement in art and literature
reacted strongly against the scientific rationalism of the eighteenth century which had played such an important part in
securing the development and utilization of the steam engine.
This accounts for the curious ambivalence, almost a love–hate
relationship, between the Victorians and steam power. The
practical men, the industrialists and administrators, were all
convinced of its value. But the literary intelligentsia bred an
attitude of distasteful aloofness which is apparent in the works
of Scott, Ruskin and Matthew Arnold, when the subject was
mentioned at all, and many novelists and poets managed to avoid
it completely. Sir Walter Scott blamed most of the ills of society
on the steam engine in 1820:

> The unhappy dislocation which has taken place betwixt the
> employer and those in his employment has been attended
> with very fatal consequences. Much of this is owing to the
> steam engine.[6]

He went on to argue that this had been brought about by the
transfer to steam power causing an unwholesome concentration
of workers in towns and factories. A few authors, such as Samuel
Butler, went to the extreme of rejecting the machine civilization
altogether. Butler brilliantly lampooned the devotion of his contemporaries to machines in general and to the steam engine in

particular, seeing the latter as capable of evolving into a superior machine which could make man redundant:

> It may be granted that man's body is as yet the more versatile of the two, but then man's body is an older thing; give the vapour-engine but half the time that man has had, give it also a continuance of our present infatuation, and what may it not ere long attain to?[7]

By the end of the nineteenth century an influential group of Romantic authors led by William Morris advocated a return to a more simple sort of society than that of late Victorian England, and revived the almost lost arts of industrial craftsmanship in place of what they saw as the tasteless bric-à-brac of machine-powered mass production.

Even at the time of its greatest influence, therefore, the steam engine did not receive general praise, although there were a growing number of authors and artists who were anxious to interpret sympathetically the rhythms of the steam engine. This was outstandingly the case with the locomotive engine, which with its astonishing speed and gift of easy transport caught the imagination of most observers. J. M. W. Turner sought to catch the new wonder in paint with his 'Rain, Steam and Speed', and many others drew and wrote about the railway locomotive. There were also a handful of authors who strove to express the positive values of the progressive, machine-based society. Rudyard Kipling and H. G. Wells both made contributions of this sort.[8] Their efforts supported the work of three generations of encyclopaedists, lecturers on science and technology, and authors of practical manuals, whose praise for the steam engine had been consistent throughout the nineteenth century.

The ambitious *Cyclopaedia* produced in 39 volumes by Abraham Rees in 1819 devoted ninety pages to an article on the 'Steam-Engine or Fire-Engine', which provided an excellent historical introduction followed by a detailed technical exposition. Discussing the manufacture of engines this article said:

> The great demand for these machines, which has taken place since their value has been so fully understood, has occasioned them to be manufactured in a large way by several engineers, who adopt the same system as is pursued in making of watches and clocks, viz. that of having workmen instructed in making

the separate parts, and employing machines and tools for every operation which admits of such aid.[9]

It went on to consider the contributions of the leading manufacturers. The article was written by John Farey, who published in 1827 his definitive *Treatise on the Steam Engine – Historical, Practical and Descriptive*.[10] The 'Introduction' to this contained a passage of fulsome praise for the steam engine which followed closely a similar section in the Rees article:

> The steam-engine is an invention highly creditable to human genius and industry, for it exhibits the most valuable application of philosophical principles to the arts of life, and has produced greater and more general changes in the practice of mechanics, than has ever been effected by any one invention recorded in history . . . All other inventions appear insignificant when compared with the modern steam-engine . . . The steam-engine follows next to the ship in the scale of inventions, when considered in reference to its utility, and as an instance of the persevering ingenuity of man, to bend the powers of nature to his will, and employ their energies to supply his real and artificial wants; but when we consider the steam-engine as a production of genius, it must be allowed to take the lead of all other inventions.

The paean of superlatives was taken up a few years later by Andrew Ure, whose study of *The Philosophy of Manufactures* was published in 1835.[11] Dr Ure was an unstinting admirer of free enterprise and industrialization, and his book was intended as a defence and justification of the factory system which had recently begun to come under criticism in the debates about factory legislation. Describing the excellencies of the typical cotton factory, he attributed many of its best qualities to the steam engine:

> In those spacious halls the benignant power of steam summons around him his myriads of willing menials, and assigns to each the regulated task, substituting for painful muscular effort on their part, the energies of his own gigantic arm, and demanding in return only attention and dexterity to correct such little aberrations as casually occur in his workmanship. The gentle docility of this moving force qualifies it for impelling the tiny bobbins of the lace machine with a precision

and speed inimitable by the most dexterous hands, directed
by the sharpest eyes . . .

Ure was not primarily concerned with statistics and provided little
quantifiable material about steam power. But his contemporary,
G. R. Porter, was compiling facts and figures which supplied the
basis for the work which was first published in a single volume
in 1847 although it had been issued in serial form over the
previous ten years. This was *The Progress of the Nation*, a
book which was very popular and went through many subsequent
editions. Referring to the introduction of steam power to
Manchester, he claimed that

> . . . In the year 1800, the number of such engines in that town
> had increased to 32, the aggregate power of which was estimated
> as equal to the labour of 430 horses.[12]

Porter went on to state:

> The steam power newly provided in 1835 in the cotton dis-
> tricts of Lancashire and its immediate vicinity, was . . . more
> than seventeen times as great as the whole steam power in
> use in Manchester at the beginning of the century . . .[13]

He supported this with a table which indicated that in 1835, out
of 987 cotton factories for which returns were available, there
were 1,000 steam engines generating 27,433 hp, and 479 water
wheels giving 6,575 hp with a labour force of 172,605.

An eloquent statement of the powerful impression of the steam
engine on public opinion at the middle of the nineteenth century
can be found in a review of various works on the physical sciences
in the *Quarterly Review*. It contains the following passage:

> In alluding to the connexion of physical knowledge with the
> arts of life, we cannot pass over the Steam Engine in its
> various forms, as the transcendant instance of what has been
> attained in the perfection and practical uses of machinery. At
> first a comparatively rude and powerless application of a
> natural agent, it has now, by a consummate adaptation of
> parts, and the removal of all that can impair or disturb its
> action, become the most powerful, as well as most certain and
> controllable minister of man – carrying him at the speed of
> fifty miles an hour along his railways – stemming the wildest
> storms of the Atlantic – draining the deepest mines, and

converting the great lake of Haarlem to dry land – or giving continuous and orderly motion to the complex myriad of wheels which perform the work of a Manchester cotton-mill. Familiar as these things now are to our daily view, they would have served as material for the fairy tales of our fore-fathers. And in every point they singularly exemplify what we are now describing, viz. the great power which man has gained over the natural world and its most uncontrollable elements, by the variety of combinations and exactness of methods which are characteristic of modern science.[14]

With the number of steam engines increasing so rapidly, and with the continuous development in types and techniques of construction, there was a growing need for manuals which could explain their features to the artisans who had to make and service them. Typical of such mid-nineteenth-century handbooks was John Bourne's *Treatise on the Steam Engine*, first published in 1846. The lavish dedication of this book by Bourne to Her Majesty Queen Victoria may be regarded as the apotheosis of praise for the steam engine, so many beneficent features of civilization were attributed to that

> . . . great mechanical agent which has fought the battles of the empire, and now sustains its greatness; which binds nations together in amity, annihilates distance, softens national prejudices, and promotes civilization; which British artizans have brought to its present perfection . . .[15]

These were sentiments which later found tangible expression in the Great Exhibition of 1851. They demonstrate the confidence and exuberance which British engineers had acquired as a result of their supremacy in the technology of steam power by the middle of the nineteenth century.

In contrast with this host of admirers, such academics as noticed steam power at all showed little understanding of its significance. Even Arnold Toynbee, credited with the first use of the term 'Industrial Revolution' in his lectures under that title first published in 1884, mentions the steam engine only incidentally, and then in a reference to James Watt, who in 1769 'took out his patent for the steam engine'.[16] But one group of scholars did study the steam engine to good effect in the nine-teenth century. These were the scientists involved in what we now know as the study of thermodynamics. It was curiosity about the operation of the steam engine, stimulated by the careful acccounts kept of engine performances in Cornwall and the puzzling bonus in efficiency brought by using steam at higher pressures, which led mathematical theorists such as Sadi Carnot to define the laws governing the function of all heat engines. Ironically, this work was one of the influences which undermined the steam engine, for a grasp of basic thermodynamic principles led to the rise of the internal combustion engine and all that stemmed from it.[17]

Although the judgement of contemporaries about the role of the steam engine in the nineteenth century was by no means uniform, it is possible to see its contribution in retrospect more objectively and therefore more clearly, and with the benefit of such hindsight it is not unfair to characterize Victorian Britain as the Age of Steam Power. Admittedly, it was the locomotive steam engine which got most publicity, its stationary version being but rarely seen by the man in the street except by the sign of a sooty chimney and a throbbing workshop. But it was the stationary steam engine, in one of its many forms and multiplied into hundreds and thousands, which made possible the tremendous expansion of British industry by overcoming the threat of power-starvation and by making power available cheaply virtually wherever it was required. It is not necessary to reflect every nuance of Bourne's loquacious praise in order to make the point, but the point itself is beyond reasonable doubt. Such was the success of the stationary steam engine that water power, wind power, and all other sources of energy were, if not superseded, at least relegated to a marginal role in British industry. Probably no prime mover before or since has dominated a national economy as the steam engine did that of Britain in the nineteenth century. Here, outstandingly, was the apotheosis of the steam engine.

CHAPTER THREE

Decline

Whereas in 1800 the future of Britain was obscured by a devastating European war, even though certain social and economic advantages were beginning to show a promise of considerable industrial expansion and prosperity, the position in 1900 was very different. By the later date, Britain had enjoyed the power and prestige of world supremacy for the greater part of a century, and it had exercised the authority which it derived from this supremacy to police the trade routes of the world and to maintain the remarkable period of comparatively peaceful international relations known as the 'Pax Britannica'. British supremacy was not merely a patriotic illusion. It was solidly based upon spectacular advances in industrial productivity, transport systems, and power technology. In all these respects the steam engine had been an indispensable instrument, and it is therefore no exaggeration to suggest that there was, at the very least, a close correlation between the development of steam power and the rise of Britain to world ascendancy.

The correlation, however, also operated in reverse. By 1900 British supremacy was being seriously challenged for the first time since the end of the Napoleonic Wars, and it was in the process of being unseated from its position as undisputed 'workshop of the world' and 'arbiter of Europe'. It seems likely that the commitment to steam power in Britain was one element in this process. The commitment was strongest in those industries – textiles, coal, iron and steel – which came under the heaviest pressure from foreign competition in this period, and as steam plant represented such a colossal investment in these sectors it was hopelessly uneconomic to consider switching to other prime movers as they became available. Even though British scientists and inventors played a prominent part in the development of the internal combustion engine and electricity, therefore, British industry as a whole showed less flexibility in adopting these

sources of power than did continental and American industries.
Partly this was due to the comparatively small output which
could be sustained by oil engines and electricity generators until
well into the present century, so that their application to heavy
industrial services was restricted. But it was also in part the result
of a comparative tardiness on the part of the British industrialists
to switch their investments from old and well-tested industries
to new processes in engineering such as automobile manufacture.
The consequence of these related trends was that the fate of steam
power in Britain became identified with precisely those industries
and transport systems which felt most severely the effects of
foreign competition in the twentieth century. Thus the decline
of steam power, at least in the shape of the reciprocating engine,
coincided with the collapse of the cotton industry, the contraction
of the coal industry, the rationalization of the steel industry,
and the transformation of marine engineering. These industries,
like the steam engine itself, had been the staples of the British
Industrial Revolution, and their comparative eclipse in the years
after the First World War was reflected in the virtual elimination
of the stationary steam engine.

Of course, it may be argued that there is no great puzzle
about the loss of British ascendancy. Once it was recognized by
other nations that Britain had discovered a sort of Midas-touch
in the shape of rapid industralization which was capable of
changing raw materials into objects of wealth and prosperity, it
was natural enough that they should want to follow and that
they should model themselves on British development. It was
equally inevitable that as soon as such large nations as Germany
and the United States of America started on this process of
industrialization, it was only a matter of time before their superior
natural resources enabled them to overtake and pass Britain.
This point arrived about 1900. Germany, united into a common
market and a single state by the diplomacy of Bismarck, underwent rapid industrial expansion in the second half of the nineteenth
century. By the end of the century it had overtaken British
production in such vital commodities as steel, while in important
new industries such as chemicals and electrical engineering
Germany had already attained a strong position with a monopoly
in world markets for new materials such as artificial dyestuffs.
The United States, with an even larger internal market and
immense natural resources, set out to exploit these advantages

energetically after the setback of the Civil War which ended in 1865. 'The business of America is business', said one American President (Calvin Coolidge in 1925), summarizing vividly the attitude which enabled the U.S.A. not merely to overtake Britain but to emerge as the outstanding world power in the twentieth century.

In a sense, therefore, the decline of Britain from her position of world supremacy at the turn of the nineteenth and twentieth centuries was simply a matter of international logistics, according to which the other nations of Europe with France, Belgium, Switzerland and Germany leading the way, learnt the lessons of industrialization from British experience and determined to develop their own resources in the same way. They were then followed by the United States and later, in the twentieth century, by other nations such as the U.S.S.R. and Japan. The problem thus becomes not so much one of accounting for the relative decline of Britain, which seems almost inevitable once the processes of rapid industrialization had been set in motion, but rather one of accounting for the long lead held by Britain in these processes during the nineteenth century. We have already suggested an explanation for this phenomenon in terms of social needs, social resources, and a society receptive to technological innovation, and the implication of our argument is that once the efficacy of industrialization as a means to national power had been demonstrated by Britain, its example could be copied by other nations, frequently by government sponsorship of innovation, definition of needs, and commitment of resources.

But the argument is not completely convincing, firstly because it suggests an element of historical inevitability which we reject in this context, and secondly because it depends upon a 'once-for-all' view of industrialization whereby a nation which has crossed the charmed threshold then has nothing to do except wait for the other nations to join it. In fact, we now know that industrialization and the vast process of social transformation which accompanies it does not terminate at any predetermined point but continues for as long as any society chooses to pursue the objective of increasing productivity. International events in the twentieth century, despite the dislocations of two World Wars, have demonstrated a capacity for continuing and apparently indefinite development towards increasing productivity and wealth on the part of the leading industrial nations, and the relatively underdeveloped nations have shown great anxiety to embark on the same course. Any appearance of stagnation in mid-stream is thus either the result of different relative speeds of development, or of an actual faltering in the pace of change, or of a combination of the two. It now seems fairly clear that British experience at the end of the nineteenth century represents such a combination, with the rise of other industrial nations coinciding with internal factors which amounted to a failure to recognize and exploit the opportunities of a changing situation. Economic historians have debated at length the so-called 'Great Depression' of the 1880s and 1890s, and many have decided to dismiss it as a myth.[1] Yet the sense that somewhere around this period Britain experienced a 'climacteric', that it adjusted too slowly and rather painfully to a new world situation, persists. British industrialists and investors went on backing those industries – cotton, coal, iron and steel – which had been the dominant boom sectors of the Industrial Revolution, and were reluctant to shift resources to new products and processes. There was a sort of lethargy here, compounded of past successes, conservatism, and complacency. It was both as a cause and a consequence of this attitude that they continued to depend on steam power and, more particularly, on the reciprocating steam engine. The next stage of industrialization depended upon other sources of energy, and British reluctance to recognize this fact constricted its development at just the time when other countries without the same commitment to steam technology were beginning to take advantage of internal combustion and electricity.

It should be said most emphatically that the transition with which we are concerned here did not involve the decline of steam power as such. Steam power has increased in the twentieth century, with the construction of ever-larger steam turbines to generate electricity, whether their boilers be fired by coal, oil, or atomic fuels. But steam turbines come only peripherally within our terms of reference, and their story is not yet a pressing matter of industrial archaeological examination. It is the reciprocating steam engine which concerns us, and it is this which has been made obsolete in the present century. The process of obsolescence, however, has been a very gradual one in Britain, and the reciprocating steam engine has contributed significantly to the success of the other prime movers which have replaced it. This service is seen most clearly in the development of electricity as a widespread source of power. An early problem of the electrical engineers, and one which long delayed the application of electricity, was that of securing a high speed of rotation for their generators, in order to achieve sufficient economy with compactness and minimum vibration to make their plant attractive.[2] Although long adapted for rotary action, the traditional reciprocating engine was not built for the high speeds required by electrical engineering, even with high gear ratios, so the steam engineers applied themselves to providing an engine which would meet this need. There were several successful answers of which the enclosed self-lubricating inverted vertical engines were the most widely used reciprocating forms. The best of these were the Willans central-valve engine, extensively used in early British power stations, and the Belliss & Morcom engines, of which a good number remain in use for small stand-by generating units in factories, hospitals and other institutions.

These reciprocating types were eventually superseded for all large-scale power generating by the steam turbine. In regions where geography permits the use of water turbines, hydro-electric power has been an attractive substitute for steam, but otherwise all large power stations have turned to the steam turbine. This sprang from British steam technology, Charles Parsons being the inventor of the first commercially successful design in 1884. Direct rotary action had long been an aspiration of steam engineers, and in the shape of the 'aeolopile' made by Hero of Alexandria in the second century A.D. a steam reaction turbine may fairly be regarded as the first working steam engine. James Watt had considered a design for an engine in which steam acted on rotor blades enclosed in a casing, but he had been dissatisfied with the results and concentrated on improving his reciprocating designs.[3] The introduction of high-pressure steam gave fresh impetus to experiments in this field, and patents were taken out in Britain and America for various designs, none of which achieved any commercial success.[4] Not until Parsons's model of 1884 were the problems of efficient steam-turbine construction overcome, and it took another decade to market the new commodity, both as an electricity generator and as a form of marine screw propulsion, in both of which fields it quickly won resounding successes. Much of the subsequent development of the steam turbine took place in America and continental Europe, and in any case the story moves beyond the boundaries of our subject. Suffice it to say once more that in the shape of the steam turbine, steam power still enjoys a very vigorous life and makes an enormous contribution to the power needs of the modern world.

The role of the reciprocating steam engine in the development of the internal combustion engine is less direct than its part in electric power generation, but it is none the less significant. In the shape of the cannon, internal combustion as a source of energy has a longer history than that of the reciprocating steam engine, and success with the cannon stimulated experiments with gunpowder engines in the seventeenth century. The problem, however, of obtaining more than one useful stroke from such an engine remained insuperable until the availability of town gas as a source of fuel in the nineteenth century, and this led to intensive research into the possibilities of internal combustion. It is a mistake to imagine that the reciprocating steam engine was without rivals, even in Britain in the early nineteenth century. The persistent experiments with direct-rotary steam engines have already been mentioned, and an even more revolutionary conception was that of the hot-air engine, a British design of which was first patented by James Stirling in 1827, which produced useful work from the pressure differences in a mass of air heated and cooled alternately. The full potential of this design has not yet been fulfilled, partly because other prime movers have been more easily available, but for light duties such as operating fans hot-air engines were used in the nineteenth century.

These attempts to improve upon the reciprocating steam engine were closely related to the increasing theoretical understanding of heat engines in general. We have noted how the study of thermodynamics developed in the first half of the nineteenth century, stimulated by the experience of steam power and particularly the detailed recording of Cornish engine performances which provided a fund of mathematical data and demonstrated that high-pressure steam was even more economical than would have been imagined if it had been seen as merely using the steam more economically. In fact, the temperature differential between the high- and the low-pressure steam produced a bonus of increased power, which led to the realization that heat energy 'flowed' through a heat engine in a way analogous to water over a water wheel, and that the greater the 'fall' the more the energy that could be derived from it. This in

turn led to the clarification and identification of the concepts of
'work', 'power', and 'energy' and the formulation of the ideas
of the conservation of energy and of entropy.

Although based in large measure upon the study of the steam
engine in its reciprocating form, the science of thermodynamics
made little contribution to the further refinement of this type
of engine. Indeed, by the mid-nineteenth century, when the
laws of thermodynamics were being formulated, the reciprocating steam engine had already more or less attained its maximum
design efficiency, worked out on the basis of earlier and more
primitive ideas of energy and on a great deal of inspired empirical
development and modification. The invention of the uniflow
engine and the introduction of forced lubrication were to show
that improvements were still possible, but there was no scope for
fundamental innovation in the reciprocating steam engine once
the techniques of high-pressure steam had been fully mastered.
But having been fostered, as it were, by the steam engine, the
new science soon began to influence the course of research on
other prime movers, and especially that on internal combustion
using town gas, oil and petrol as fuels, and burning these to
drive a piston in a cylinder of the type familiar to generations
of steam engineers. Once problems of producing a combustible
vapour and of firing it at rapid intervals had been overcome, the
way was clear for the development of an efficient engine and was
achieved through the work of Lenoir, Otto and many others.
Using oil fuels it was quickly appreciated that engines of this
type had a potential flexibility of operation which made them
ideal for compact locomotive units, so that the automobile and
the aeroplane emerged to take advantage of it. Meanwhile,
continuing study of the thermal efficiency of internal combustion
led engineers such as Crossleys in Manchester to introduce successful engines in the 1870s, and Ackroyd Stuart to improve the
oil engine further, while Rudolf Diesel eventually developed the
high-compression oil engine which followed the principles of
thermodynamics to give a very efficient heavy-duty engine.

Within a mere half century, therefore, the internal combustion
engine advanced from a very primitive experimental form to a
highly efficient and sophisticated prime mover. It had seemed
suitable, in its early days, for light duties to supplement steam
engines or for use in small workshops where it did not need to
be run all the time. Many gas engines and oil engines were

installed in Britain for these purposes, and in continental Europe and America they were adopted with even more enthusiasm because of their greater flexibility of operation than the steam engine; and in America, because of the cheapness of oil fuels following the pioneering efforts of Rockefeller and his Standard Oil Company in extracting oil and distributing it on a colossal scale. Also, it should be remembered that in these areas the steam engine did not have the same assured dominance that it had attained in Britain, so that the emergence of an alternative was greeted with less suspicion, not to say enthusiasm. Then, at the turn of the new century, the internal combustion engine began to challenge even heavy-duty steam engines in road traction, agricultural machinery, marine engines, and industry. The great mill steam engines retained their predominance for another couple of decades, and some very large reciprocating units continued to be installed in rolling mills in Germany, two being built after 1945. But in virtually every other respect the reciprocating steam engine lost ground in competition with internal combustion. Again, it was in America, Germany and elsewhere on the Continent, that the heavy oil-type engine won its first successes in farm tractors and submarines; but its advantages over steam gradually secured its victory even in Britain. Meanwhile, even the mill engines, winding engines and pumping engines, the last bastions of reciprocating steam, were challenged and replaced by both internal combustion and electric power. In the last resort, the steam engine has lost out primarily on grounds of flexibility. Whereas internal combustion engines and electric motors can be switched on and off as required, and can be moved about relatively easily, the steam engine requires a boiler and a boiler-man and thus becomes much more of a fixture. With the rising cost of labour, it is particularly the greater human attention required by the steam engine which has weighed against it in the minds of industrialists and transport operators.

Any interpretation of the complex changes in the internal pattern of industrial activities in Britain since the beginning of the present century needs thus to take into account the radical shift in the international status of the country, and the comparative rigidity with which Britain clung to the staple industries which had served it so well in the past. This inflexibility was understandable in so far as it involved a heavy capital commitment to plant and equipment in these well-established industries, and also a strong sentimental commitment to industries which were, after all, still prosperous in 1900 despite some portents of future change. The stationary steam engine represented part of both the capital commitment and the sentimental commitment, and it continued to serve well those industries to which it had made the greatest contribution until they were undermined by other forces over which the provision of efficient prime movers had little influence. It should be added, moreover, that British industrialists may have been a little slow in switching their investments to new industries and new sources of power, but they did make the switch, and in the years after the First World War the possibilities of the automobile, electric traction, the heavy oil engine and the aeroplane, were vigorously exploited. What is at issue, therefore, is not a long-term failure of invention or initiative. Indeed, there was hardly any failure of inventive activity, as is shown by the remarkable contribution of British pioneers to the technology of internal combustion and electrical engineering. What is significant is the comparative unresponsiveness of Britain in the period 1880–1914 to pressures to develop in new fields and with new techniques, and its preference for well-tried industries and processes of which the continued commitment to the reciprocating steam engine was a striking symptom.

Illustrations of this unresponsive attitude of British opinion abound in both the technical and the general literature of the period, but a few examples must suffice to make the point. Note, for instance, some of the editorial comments of *The Engineer* around the turn of the century:

> We have consistently contended that the advantages claimed for electricity had never been proved, whilst its disadvantages were sufficiently patent to everyone but the electrical engineer.[5]

This, to be fair, was in the course of welcoming an American report which was critical of the use of electrical auxiliary equipment in the U.S. Navy, but its tone is symptomatic of the complacency of the period, even though it was undoubtedly true that the promised advantages of electric power had at that time still to be demonstrated in practice. It was only when British supremacy in steam technology seemed in danger that the comments became agitated, as in the poor performance at the Paris Exhibition of 1900:

> But it is when one approaches the English section among the steam engines that the patriotic reporter feels desperate, and his heart grows faint.[6]

By the beginning of the next year, however, complacency was temporarily restored:

> Not the least instructive lesson taught by the events of the last century is that we have mainly reached our present position by trial and error, and that little or nothing has originated by the aid of mathematical science. The original thinker, who has been able to reduce his thoughts to practice, has done the world's work. The bookman has followed afterwards and explained why it is that the doer has succeeded.[7]

One such bookman, R. Scott Burn, introducing a practical manual by various writers on *The Steam Engine User* (London, 1894), was true to form:

> The reader may rest assured that, in spite of the sanguine vaticinations of some of our engineers, it is not the present generation, and if the signs be read aright which are open to us, possibly not the next, or even the generation succeeding that, which will see the steam engine so universally superseded as to make a paper of this kind no longer a necessity.[8]

The reference to 'some of our engineers' who thought otherwise is significant, but it is unlikely that they had a wide following although the journal *Engineering* gave expression to some of their doubts about the continuing reign of steam power:

> The supremacy which the steam engine has so long enjoyed is now assailed from two sides. The water turbine and the gas engine have become dangerous rivals; and there are those who assert that early in the twentieth century we may expect to find the steam engine ousted from its place as the most economical prime mover by one or other of these later forms of power generator.[9]

This was in the course of a report on a paper at the British Association meeting by Mr J. B. C. Kershaw, who had made a careful analysis of the costs of power generation. It would be useful if

comparative statistical data of the development of steam power
in the leading nations over this period could be compiled, but no
such compilation is at present available, and in default of such
quantification we may suggest from the sort of impressionistic
evidence quoted here that British opinion was responding, but
responding comparatively sluggishly, to the challenges presented
by the new sources of power. Still, it was becoming clear that
the twentieth-century future lay largely in these new fields, and
from the First World War onwards Britain has been exploiting
them as much as the other advanced industrial nations.

The result has been that in Britain, as elsewhere, the decline
of the reciprocating steam engine has been rapid and virtually
complete: only in Britain it has been somewhat slower, owing
to the affection for the steam engine which has been widely
regarded as a good reliable friend of long standing, not to be
lightly put aside since it was highly economical as far as fuel
was concerned and there was little capital available for electric
driving schemes at marginal economies; and also, because there
was such a heavy concentration of steam engines in Britain,
their removal has taken more time than elsewhere. In terms of
industrial archaeology, this means that the reciprocating steam
engine has reached that moment of complete obsolescence which
makes it outstandingly ripe for investigation; and such investigation has become a matter of considerable urgency because of
the rapid disappearance of steam engines. For all that, Britain
has a good selection of engines which can be visited and studied,
and we have set out the main specimens in Part III. Lack of space
and personal experience has led us to exclude other countries
from our list, but of course steam engines have been used throughout the world and may be found in all sorts of outlandish places,
some of them doubtless still at work. Many important engines
have been preserved in the U.S.A., including a goodly number
from Britain. Henry Ford fortunately did not practise what he
preached, for despite his notorious judgement that 'History is
bunk' he went to great expense to assemble a collection of steam
engines in his museum at Dearborn, Michigan, and it is a good
job that he did so, because most of these engines would certainly
have gone for scrap had it not been for his perceptive interest
and pioneering industrial archaeological activity.

Other museum collections all over the world, although none on
the Henry Ford scale, have preserved engines of a wide variety

of types. All over the world, also, where Cornish engineers have spread Cornish mining techniques – in the U.S.A., in Latin America, in South Africa, and in Australia, Cornish engine houses survive, occasionally with their giant pumping engines and whims inside. India and other countries which were part of the British Empire in the nineteenth and twentieth centuries received large numbers of British steam engines, both locomotives for their railways and stationary engines for their waterworks, mills, foundries and steam boats. Although we know of no detailed research on the survival of these machines it seems likely that many will still exist and may even be at work. Certainly many of the locomotive steam engines still run on the railways of the Far East, as they do in some East European countries; so even though the reciprocating steam engine has lost much ground, it is taking an unconscionable time a-dying, a fact which is a credit to the robustness of the design and the skill of the manufacturers, most of whom are no longer available to supply spares and new parts.

Whatever the future of the reciprocating steam engine – and there remains a good possibility that for certain duties in some parts of the world it will continue to give good service for many years to come – there is thus a great deal of work to be done on recording and assessing the role of the engine, not only in Britain, but throughout the world. This is particularly the case with the stationary engine, for whereas its locomotive brother has received a lot of publicity and attention, the formidable contributions of the stationary steam engine to industrial productivity as the effects of the Industrial Revolution have swept across the world have been comparatively neglected although they have been incalculable. Or, at least, they cannot be calculated until much more work has been done on their distribution and use, on the manufacturers who produced them, and on the engineers who erected, maintained and modified them. Although so late in the day, the fact that this task of industrial archaeological scholarship has at last begun means that there is a chance that historical justice will be done to the stationary steam engine.

PART TWO

The Techniques of Steam Power

CHAPTER FOUR

Mechanical Principles

INTRODUCTION

Having surveyed the evolution of the reciprocating steam engine and its role in the British Industrial Revolution, we turn in this section to consider some of the more technical aspects of the development of steam power in order to help the industrial archaeologist to know what to look for and to understand what he sees. A period of evolution is always an exciting one from a technical point of view, as active minds are exercised to find their own 'best' solutions to the difficulties and defects which soon become evident in either the working or the construction of a new functional mechanism. This applies outstandingly to the steam engine, so that the first fifty years of the mill engine (1790–1840), and a rather later period in the case of the marine engine (1810–60), saw the introduction and trial of an immense range of designs, each contributing to the development of the steam engine.

One of the continuing themes of this development has been the search for economy. As the fuel consumption of a steam engine is reduced when the operating pressure is raised, since the steam can be expanded and made to do work down to the lowest temperature (pressure), the story of the steam engine has been largely that of exploiting this possibility, as advances in constructional techniques have permitted higher working steam pressures. Thus the Newcomen engine worked with steam at atmospheric pressure, using only the vacuum, and this was followed by Watt's engine, which used steam up to 5 psi, each of these types requiring a large supply of cooling water to achieve effective condensation of the steam. The next step was made around 1800, when both Trevithick and Evans raised the steam pressure to 50 or 100 psi, making powerful engines which could operate without a condenser or vacuum. The fairly elementary constructional techniques of the period made such pressures

c

dangerous, and following several boiler explosions, pressures in Britain settled to a gradual increase to 20 psi in the 1840s, rising to 30–50 psi in the 1860s, to 100–120 psi in the 1880s, and on to 180–200 psi by the end of the century. There were, however, a limited number of designs, such as the early steam road carriages, which used steam up to 100 psi in the 1830s, and those of Jacob Perkins and other members of his family, who were successfully generating and using steam at 500 psi by the 1870s.

The high temperatures and the need for surfaces in contact to maintain steam tightness together with the customary boilers with their large size and water content, long restricted the introduction of higher pressures. It was the introduction of the water-tube boiler with its small-sized parts and limited water content, and the steam turbine with no working surfaces in contact, which later paved the way for the dramatic rises in pressure and temperature, with ever-increasing economy, in the twentieth century, so that regular steam pressures have now risen to 3,000 psi, and the temperatures sometimes exceed 1,000°F.

The development of the steam engine thus became largely a matter of producing boilers to generate high-pressure steam, and engines able to utilize it with a minimum of internal loss. If high-pressure steam was admitted for only a part of the stroke, it would expand and give useful work for the remainder of the stroke by losing heat and pressure, and since the (steam and) cylinder was cooled in the process, the hot steam was also cooled when admitted for the next stroke, so that there was a continuing struggle to reduce these effects. This attempt followed three broad lines of development: first, staged expansion, in which the steam was expanded in two, three, or four cylinders in turn, so reducing the temperature drop in each; second, steam jacketing, in which the cylinders were encased in steam of the admission pressure (temperature), or heat was added to the steam before admission (superheating) or between the cylinders (reheating); and third, improvements in the design of valves and passages by which the steam was transferred throughout the working cycle. The ultimate in this process was the uniflow engine in which, as in the turbine, the steam moved in one direction only, so that cooling only occurred as a result of doing work, together with a very small amount from radiation.

Although this emphasis on increasing efficiency was common to all aspects of steam-engine development, there were other criteria which had to be considered and which were in some circumstances more important than mechanical efficiency. The locomotive engine, for instance, required limited power but had to carry its fuel and water with it, so that it was restricted by the carrying capacity of the rails as to the amount of these which it could load, although both fuel and water were normally available at short intervals. Even more limiting were the conditions under which marine engines operated, as these had not only to carry fuel for ten days or more, but also the large staffs of men needed to service them and their boilers, although cooling water was no problem at sea. The emphasis in marine engines was thus on maximum power and fuel economy, so that some of the Cunard paddle vessels were already using nearly 4,000 hp by the 1860s, while by the early 1870s naval engines of HMS *Hercules* and other ships developed nearly 9,000 hp on their trials, and marine steam engines exploited to the full the possibilities of staged expansion with compound, triple, and quadruple arrangements. In comparison with locomotive and marine engines, stationary engines for mills and other duties had less difficulty with fuel and water, and less limitation on weight and size, so that they offered more scope for experiment and development.

The simple linear mechanism of the direct-acting steam engine developed through many stages and designs, most of which are represented by models or examples in the Science Museum, London, and other museums. Following upon Watt's invention of the double-acting engine in 1782, most steam engines other than the Cornish pumping engines were of this type until 1870, with even the smallest rarely running at more than 90 rpm. However, in the 1860s two inventions came from the United States which were to have far-reaching effects on steam engines. These were the Corliss valve and valve gear, and the Porter Allen high-speed engine. The latter was provided with separate flat slide valves for the steam inlet and the exhaust at each end (that is, four valves to each cylinder), and the engine was able to run at very high speeds even though it was not enclosed. (See below, p. 77.) In the 1870s a number of high-speed engines were designed in Britain by Brotherhood, Halsey and others. One, the Willans, was to become very important in the budding electricity industry, and probably more horse power was made by this than by any other single-acting design which, in the U.K. at least, were little developed, except the Brotherhood engine for torpedo propulsion. These engines were all enclosed and single-acting, since it was considered that a double-acting engine would knock itself to pieces rapidly at such speeds, and it was not until 1890 that the first satisfactory high-speed double-acting engine was developed by Belliss & Morcom. This engine was enclosed and lubricated with oil under pressure, and many thousands were made for almost every service. They were still being made for export in the 1960s. Such engines frequently ran for over a year without stopping.

ENGINE STRUCTURE

One basic chain of events applied to all reciprocating steam engines, whatever variety of mechanical linkage was used between the piston thrust and the rotating crankshaft. Fig. 1 illustrates this basic train. It comprised the piston 'P' upon which the steam (and/or atmospheric/vacuum) pressure acted, which was usually circular and worked within a cylinder 'C'. This transmitted the effort 'T' to the piston rod 'PR', and so to the crosshead 'CD', the effort so far being a simple linear one. To convert this to rotative action, a swinging lever or connecting rod 'CR' was used which was attached to 'CD' at one end, performing a linear movement, and to the crank 'CK' at the other end, this being a rotating lever attached to the crankshaft.

Simple though it is, this train of movements developed several fascinating side effects of varying velocities and velocity ratios, such as the fact that the two ends of the same connecting rod were subjected to completely different movements and stresses; but we cannot consider these in detail here. The effort applied to the crank was not constant, varying throughout the revolution both from the piston thrust, reversing twice on each stroke, and from the leverage of the crank as it rotated. Since normally the resistance of the machinery driven was fairly constant, a steady effort was demanded from the engine, and so irregularities were smoothed out by the flywheel 'FW', the inertia of which resisted the tendency of the crankshaft speed to vary with the load and the effort applied. Wherever the direction of a linear thrust is changed, as with the connecting rod, a side thrust develops at the point of change, and a guiding structure is necessary to maintain the piston rod in a straight line. The guides 'G' provided this control. The power was transmitted from the crankshaft to the machines by gearing, or from the flywheel or a pulley by ropes or belts, and any tendency for the engine to gain or lose speed as the load varied was checked by the governor 'GV' which, by the mass of the revolving weights, increased or reduced the steam supply as the speed varied. Another method to secure smooth running was to couple two or three engines together, with the cranks at angles to each other.

While this was the basic mechanical train by which the piston thrust was converted into a useful effort, there were four variants on it:

1. In the beam engine (Figs. 2, 9, 10, 11 and 13) the effort was applied to a lever (the beam) and delivered in a variety of ways by interchanging the positions of the delivery of the effort to and from the beam.

2. In the return connecting rod type (Fig. 3) the connecting rod linkage, instead of proceeding in a straight line away from the initial effort, actually returned back towards it, in delivering the effort to the crankshaft. This may seem an odd procedure, but it produced several useful effects, one of which was that the engine was more compact, whilst in the table engine the connecting rod was very much longer, which reduced the side thrust on the crosshead.

3. In the oscillating type (Fig. 4), the effort was applied directly from the piston-rod end to the crankpin, which eliminated the guides and connecting rod. This, again, was very compact.

4. In the trunk type (Fig. 5) the guide mechanism was again eliminated by attaching the connecting rod directly to a gudgeon pin placed within the piston itself. This linkage, introduced by James Watt in 1784, is now an essential part of most internal combustion engines.

Apart from the beam engine, most of these arrangements only became possible as machine tools became available to produce the accurate surfaces necessary in the guides, etc. Until such machines were developed, and indeed for as long as beam engines continued to be built, parallel motions were adopted to guide the piston rod. As long as the engine was a simple pumping unit operating through a beam and stressed in one direction only, a simple chain linkage (Figs. 9 and 10) was sufficient. When, however, James Watt invented the double-acting engine in 1782, the piston rod was loaded in both directions (i.e. with a pushing as well as a pulling motion) and the connecting and guiding linkage had to be adapted to resist this. Of the many solutions which Watt invented for this purpose, the parallel motion was that which served best, and of which he was justly proud.

The first form of parallel motion (see Fig. 6) consisted of a swinging link 'A.A.' on either side of the crosshead 'CD', the motion of the ends of which was restrained to an arc by the parallel rods 'B.B.', which were attached to brackets 'F' fixed to the engine-room wall. It was a simple mechanism which was quite satisfactory at the time, but the rear links did add to the length of the engine room. Despite this feature of the three-link type, it was retained for guiding the crossheads of many vertical winding engines which were used in the Northern collieries for a century and a half, and was also adopted by James Simpson for a small number of waterworks beam engines in the 1870s. A surviving example of this linkage is in the colliery winding engine recently re-erected in the Beamish North of England Open Air Museum.

The most widely used parallel motion was Watt's later design, which consisted of a series of links arranged as a parallelogram restrained by radius rods attached to a fixed point upon the engine frame (Fig. 7). The load of the piston was again applied to the crosshead 'CD', and was transmitted to the beam by the links 'X' which results in a side thrust at 'CD'. This was controlled by fitting similar rods 'Y' which were attached to the beam at 'D', the lower parts 'A' and 'CD' being coupled together by parallel rods 'Z'. This still would not give a parallel motion at 'CD' unless the movement at 'A' was restrained to an arc, and this was done by radius rods 'W', the other ends of which were attached to the engine frame or the engine house. Plate 4 illustrates this type of parallel motion at its best, since it provides guidance for the crossheads of both the high- and the low-pressure cylinders.

Other linkages were developed to give a straight-line motion to the crosshead, and the industrial archaeologist should look out for such variations in viewing preserved engines or illustrations. The simplest of these variations was the grasshopper or half beam (Figs. 2 and 8), and was applied to beams that were attached to a

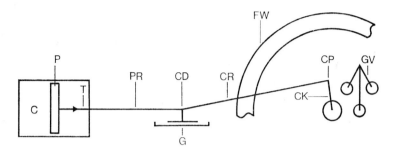

Figure 1   Steam-engine motion

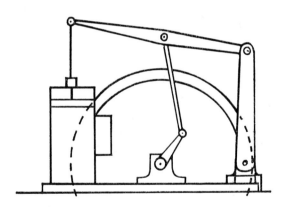

Figure 2   Grasshopper motion

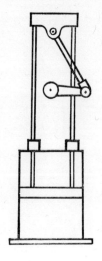

Figure 3
Return connecting
rod engine

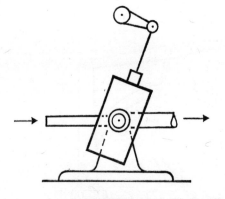

Figure 4
Oscillating engine

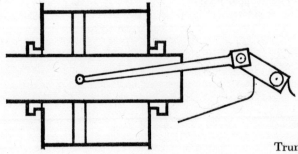

Figure 5
Trunk engine

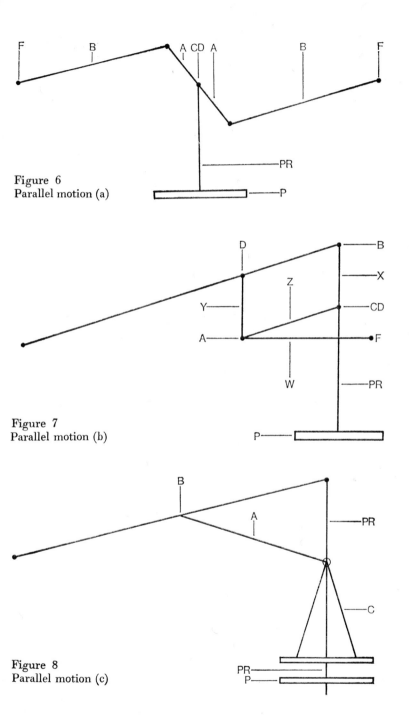

Figure 6
Parallel motion (a)

Figure 7
Parallel motion (b)

Figure 8
Parallel motion (c)

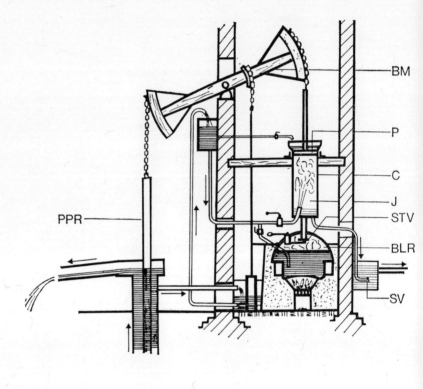

BM

P

C

J

STV

BLR

SV

PPR

Figure 9   Newcomen engine

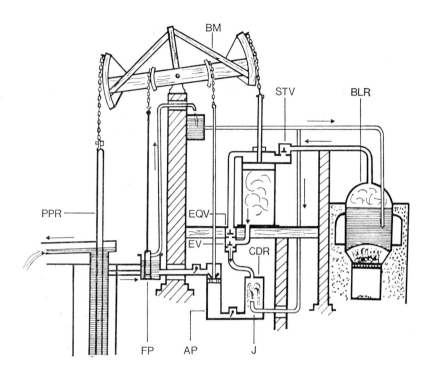

Figure 10 Watt's pumping engine

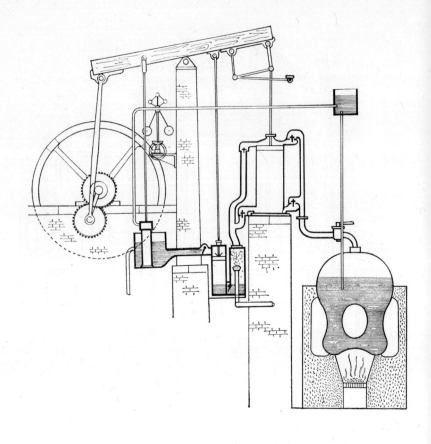

Figure 11   Watt's rotative engine

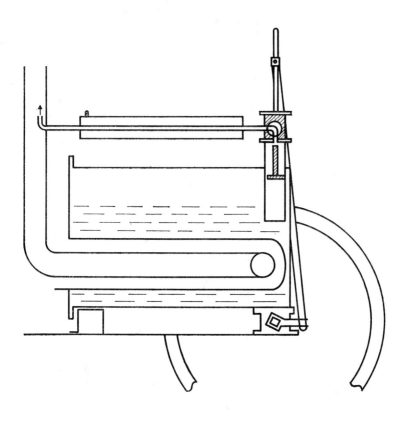

Figure 12 Trevithick's high-pressure engine

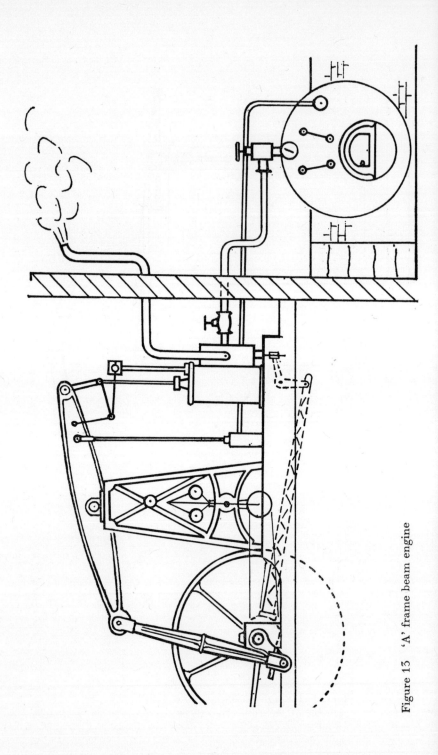

Figure 13 'A' frame beam engine

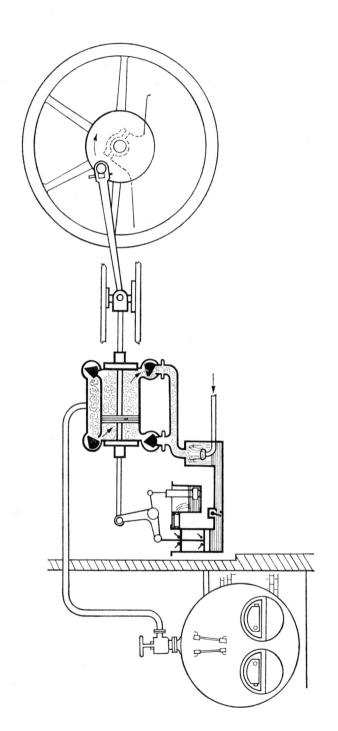

Figure 14   Horizontal single Corliss engine

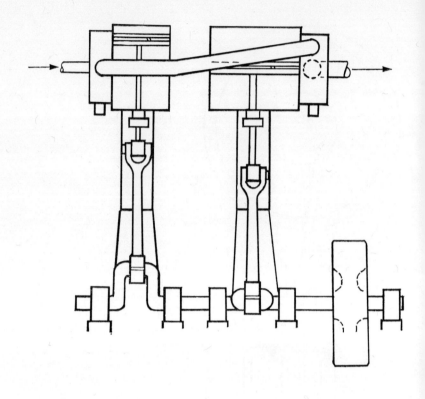

Figure 15 Inverted vertical compound engine

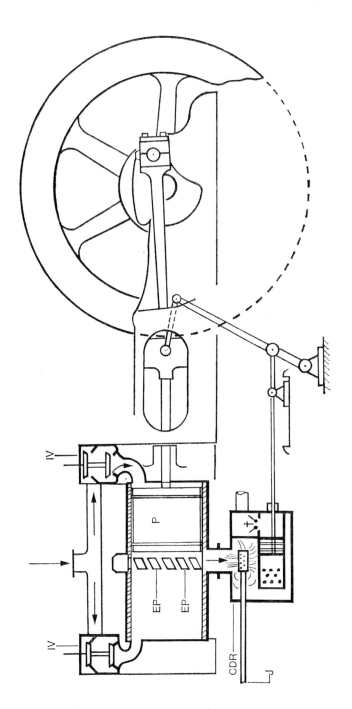

Figure 16   Uniflow engine

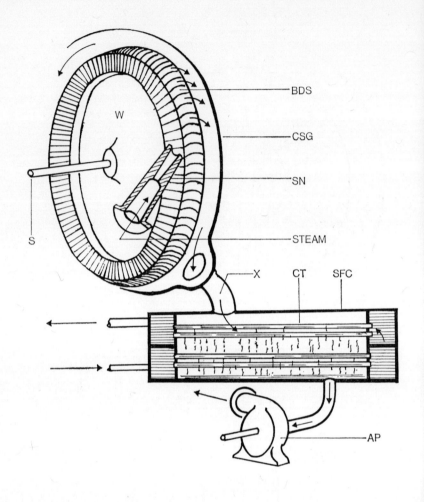

Figure 17   Steam turbine

swinging link at one end, which permitted the beam to move vertically at the other end. The parallel motion comprised a link 'A' upon either side of the beam, one end of which was attached to a pin 'B' fitted in the centre of the beam, and the other end to a pin in a bracket 'C' on the centre line of the piston rod. The engines in Plates 5 and 11 are fitted with this motion.

Another very simple motion is that shown in Plate 18. This provides the parallel motion by a single pair of links from the crosshead to the beam, and these are continued above it and maintained in parallel motion by a single pair of radius rods attached to ornate brackets upon the top of the centre column. The marine type of parallel motion, which was almost always adopted for the side-lever type of engine, can be seen in Plate 12. It was very light, yet quite satisfactory when fitted even to the largest Cunard engine developing some 4,000 hp. In contrast, Plate 13 is of a later engine in which, although of the beam type, plain guides are fitted instead of parallel motion.

EVOLUTION OF THE MECHANISM

Now that we have established the basic structure of the steam engine, we will examine the steps by which its mechanical form has evolved.

Savery 1698 The Savery engine may be regarded as the first working steam engine, but it required no machinery as such since the steam pressure acted directly upon the water being pumped. Its operation therefore only needed valves to control the events, with manually operated plug-cocks for the steam, and automatic inlet and delivery valves for the water cycle.

Newcomen 1712 The Newcomen engine is illustrated by Fig. 9. It was much more complex than the Savery engine, since it needed a cylinder and piston to produce the effort and a beam and linkages to convey it to the pump rods in the pit. The cylinder 'C' is built into the structure of the engine house and supplied with steam from the boiler 'BLR', through a valve 'STV' in the pipe between them. The piston 'P' was connected to the beam by flat link chains and the 'sector' (the wooden arc on the end of the beam), and the pump rods 'PPR' were similarly driven from the other end. The pump rods were very heavy, and as soon as steam was admitted below the piston, the weight pulled the piston to the top of the cylinder, when steam was shut off. A jet of cold water 'J' was then admitted into the cylinder, which produced a vacuum beneath the piston by condensing the steam, and the pressure of the atmosphere on the top face of the piston then overcame the weight of the pump rods and water, forcing the piston to the bottom of the cylinder, to begin another stroke. The condensed water drained away from the cylinder and any air was expelled through a 'snifting valve' 'SV' as the steam was admitted to break the vacuum. Although many improvements were made in this type of engine to reduce the heat losses, the basic cycle remained unchanged in all Newcomen engines, and the last one ceased work over two centuries after its invention.

Watt 1768 This cycle was specifically designed to avoid the heat losses caused by the water jet in the cylinder of the Newcomen engine, and is illustrated by Fig. 10. It was a great deal more complex than Newcomen's arrangement, since it required a separate condensing chamber and air pump, although it was still only a simple water pump. The steam was admitted through the steam valve 'STV' above the piston. Although at little more than atmospheric pressure, this performed the function of the atmosphere in the Newcomen engine, for together with the vacuum below the piston it overcame the weight of the pump rods and forced the piston to descend. At the bottom of the stroke, the steam and exhaust valves were closed and the equilibrium valve 'EQV' was opened, thus balancing the pressure between the top and bottom faces of the piston and drawing the steam from the former to the latter. The piston rose under the weight of the pump rods, the equilibrium valve was closed, and to make the next stroke the exhaust valve 'EV' was opened, drawing the steam into the condenser to create a vacuum below the piston, and simultaneously more steam was admitted through the steam valve above the piston. The cold condenser was thus isolated from the hot cylinder, and always under vacuum, so that the water could not drain away, and a separate air-pump 'AP' was thus provided to remove it.

Watt 1782 Fig. 11 illustrates the principles of double-action and rotation. When Watt invented the rotative double-acting cycle the mechanical train became more complex since the simple reciprocation of the beam had to be converted into rotary motion at the crankshaft while the connecting linkage of the piston rod and beam had to resist thrust in both directions. He invented the parallel motion to deal with the latter problem (Figs. 6 and 7), but when he came to use the crank to give rotary motion he was forestalled by a patent. He invented several alternatives to the crank, the most widely used of which was the 'sun and planet' motion shown in Fig. 11. This consisted of a gear wheel attached to the bottom of the connecting rod solidly so that it could not rotate, and this meshed into a similar gear wheel fixed on to the crankshaft, with a link between the two gear wheels to keep them in mesh. The sun and planet motion was abandoned some twenty years later for new engines, although it was used on one engine for a century. It had the advantage that the shaft rotated twice for each double stroke of the piston.

Trevithick 1803 Trevithick greatly simplified the mechanical train of the steam engine when, by raising steam pressure, he made it possible to work powerful engines by such pressure alone, i.e. without a vacuum and the large supply of cooling water necessary for the condensation process. By making his high-pressure engine compact and dispensing with the beam he also made it portable and suitable for locomotive purposes. There is an example of this design in the Science Museum (Fig. 12).

Independent Beam *c.* 1800 Engines such as that illustrated in Fig. 11 were substantial machines and were built into the structure of the mill (they were described as 'house-built'). These required expensive building work and it was often difficult to install them in small factories which needed steam power. For such concerns the independent type of engine, which was attached to the building only by the bedplate, was a great asset, and when using higher steam pressures and operating non-condensing this type was widely used. Many sorts of framing were adopted to support the beam centre bearings, some with one column, and others with two, four, or six columns. There were also many varieties of 'A' frames, such as that shown in Fig. 13.

Grasshopper Beam *c.* 1800 Although most beam engines were built with the beam overhead and swaying about its own centre, one design which was popular for small power units was the grasshopper type, which had the beam suspended upon a swinging link at one end, with the cylinder at the opposite end and the crankshaft and connecting rod between these points (see the discussion of the parallel motion, above). Fig. 2 illustrates the outline. Plate 5 shows an engine of this type, and Plate 13 is the marine form.

Side-lever Beam *c.* **1800** The need for a low engine in marine service in order to lower the centre of gravity of the mass as much as possible led to the development of the side-lever design, in which there are two beams to each cylinder, placed at a low level on either side of the engine (Plate 12). This type was sometimes used for mill driving.

Woolf Compound Beam 1803 The first patent for expanding the steam in two cylinders in series was that of Hornblower in 1781, but there was little advantage to be gained from this with the low steam pressures which were then generally in use. Staged expansion was again patented in 1803 by Arthur Woolf, the Cornish engineer, and he also designed boilers with small steam- and water-containing parts which safely gave steam pressures high enough to make compounding (i.e. staged expansion) eco- nomical. He placed his cylinders close together at one end of the beam, and the high-pressure or smaller cylinder was thus of a shorter stroke than the low-pressure cylinder which was usually placed under the end of the beam. This layout was constructed for over a century, being popular since it permitted compound working on a single beam without requiring extra space. The last rotative beam engine installed in a waterworks in 1919 was of this type, and several have been preserved, such as those in Plates 4 and 8.

McNaught Compound 1845 In this type, the high pressure cylinder was placed at a point about half-way between the centre support columns of a beam engine and the crankshaft, with the low-pressure cylinder in its normal position at the other end of the beam. It was originally patented as a simple method of com- pounding single-cylinder beam engines, and it was probably the most useful beam-engine design developed for mill driving, since the stresses about the beam centre were opposed to each other. It became the standard form of mill beam engine since it was powerful and economical and also worked smoothly because of the balancing of the stresses. The last beam engine made for a mill in 1904 was a combination of the Woolf and McNaught types upon a single beam. At least two examples of the McNaught type are preserved, one at Glasgow Kelvingrove Museum and the other at Bradford Industrial Museum, although both are at present in store, and the Northern Mill Engines Preservation Society has saved a much rebuilt McNaught beam.

Bell Crank *c.* **1800** This was a hybrid type which, although not widely used, deserves notice. It was very compact, with a vertical cylinder placed near to the crankshaft. The piston rod drove up to a crosshead, from which long side rods came down to one end of a right-angled lever (the bell crank) on each side of the cylinder, and the drive to the crankshaft was taken at a right angle from this by horizontal connecting rods. A small number were made in the period 1800–20, and one is preserved in the Science Museum, London (though not at present exhibited). The American E. D. Leavitt designed a number in the latter part of the nineteenth century, and James Simpson of London also made several, mainly for waterworks pumping.

Direct Acting from 1797 onwards The beam was a very convenient type, giving an easy motion and facilities for working pumps from the beam as well as driving from the crankshaft. But it was not essential to drive thus, and before Watt's patents expired in 1800 other more direct-acting designs were being developed. William Murdock made an oscillating engine in the 1780s, and in 1797 Edmund Cartwright designed a vertical direct-acting engine for which he patented a metal packing for the piston and piston rod. James Sadler also designed a direct-acting vertical engine.

Vertical 1797 to the 1890s In this type the piston rod drove upwards to a crosshead and guides from which the connecting rod drove upwards to the crankshaft overhead. It was the simplest drive for a fixed cylinder and it was deservedly popular for small engines, and its good features led to its extensive use in sizes up to 200 hp in the Yorkshire textile mills. The largest examples were those for winding coal in the North-Eastern collieries, where single-cylinder engines of 60. in bore were used for winding coal from nearly 2,000 feet deep pits, and at least one engine of 68 in. bore wound coal near Sunderland for many years. Almost every design of support was adopted for the crankshaft bearings. Some were simple 'A' frames; others were two or four columns, often fluted; and a small number were built by Fairbairn and others with all the mechanism contained within a large circular casting which supported the crankshaft at the top. The smaller ones usually had guide bars for the crosshead guides, although many had a simple block to guide the piston rod, with a pitchfork connecting rod. The very large engines in the Northern collieries usually had parallel motion similar to that illustrated in Fig. 6, as can be seen on the Beamish colliery engine already mentioned.

Table 1807 onwards This design was patented by Henry Maudslay in 1807. The cylinder was vertical but unlike the simple vertical arrangement it was placed upon a table-like platform over the crankshaft, with very long connecting rods on either side which drove downwards to the crankshaft. Mainly intended for small power units, a few large ones were made, and it proved to be an easily operated and long-lived type. It was also compact, since the cylinder was between the returning side connecting rods, and if the two crankshaft bearings were mounted in the table framing it was completely self-contained.

Oscillating *c.* 1800 As Fig. 4 indicates this was mechanically the simplest of all, since the piston rod was connected directly to the crankpin bearing, and even in the largest marine examples no guides were provided for the piston rod other than a very deep gland bush. Since the piston rod followed the crankpin movement, the cylinder had to oscillate to accommodate this and the deep gland bush was fitted to reduce wear caused by the side-pressure of the moving cylinder. The inlet and exhaust pipes had also to accommodate the cylinder movement, and the steam connections were usually taken through the trunnions upon which the cylinder oscillated. Normally only small oscillating engines were used for service ashore, but they were constructed in large sizes for paddle vessels, where in one case a low-pressure oscillating cylinder of 112 in. bore which weighed over thirty tons was in service for nearly forty years on the ss *Mona's Isle III* until the vessel was scrapped in 1919. Plate 19 illustrates a small industrial engine of this type. Plate 14 is the only oscillating paddle engine preserved in Britain and is a fine example of London engineering at its best.

Trunk 1845 This type of engine (see Fig. 5) was probably the most compact of all the fixed-cylinder designs, since the connecting rod worked from a gudgeon pin placed in the centre of the

piston. It was first devised by James Watt, but it had several disadvantages, and where used on a double-acting engine the friction of the trunk glands was considerable. None the less, it was
used extensively from 1845 onwards for driving screw propellers
in naval vessels, as it became necessary for unprotected steam
ships to have as much of the engine as possible below the water-
line. Some of the largest simple expansion engines ever built,
with cylinders of 127 in. bore, were of this type and were made
for HMS *Hercules* and other naval ships in the 1860s. The type
was little used for naval service after this, but from 1870 onwards
numerous trunk piston single-acting designs were developed to
reach a peak with the Serpollet steam car and the Willans engine
in the early 1900s; and the trunk linkage now features in every
motor car.

Side Rod *c.* **1800** This was another compact type, in which the
piston rod drove to a crosshead, from which two side rods passed
down the side of the cylinder to a lower crosshead on each side,
and from these the connecting rods drove upwards to the crank
pin. Its compactness was gained at the expense of extra parts, but
as the example in the Southampton Maritime Museum demon-
strates it required very little space.

Steeple or Return Connecting Rod *c.* **1810** In this type the
piston drove to a crosshead which was part of a triangular centre
frame embracing the sweep of the crankpin, from the apex of
which the connecting rod drove back to the crankpin (Fig. 3).
Primarily a marine type, it was used for paddle-vessel propulsion,
but it was also used for naval screw vessels as long as unprotected
hulls made it necessary to keep the engines as low as possible. It
was superseded by other types for marine use after 1870. As applied to paddle-boat propulsion it was termed a 'steeple engine',
and when adopted in a horizontal form for naval vessels it was
known as a 'return connecting-rod engine'. It was also much used
in both vertical and horizontal forms for pumps, being made for
this purpose by firms such as Camerons & Pearns of Manchester
and Evans of Wolverhampton, and in this service it was often
termed the 'banjo motion' from the assumed resemblance of the
centre frame to a banjo. There is a superb model of a steeple engine in the Glasgow Museum at Kelvingrove: it is large enough
to propel a small paddle vessel.

Simple Direct Acting from c. 1810 The growing need for cheap, small engines led to the development of relatively simple types, and the growing number of small engineering workshops contributed to this trend by specializing in plain engines with simple linkages, as outlined in Figs. 1 and 14. This simple direct-acting type was readily adapted to all purposes by inclining the motion centre line to make it suitable for driving the smallest machines in dyeworks or the largest paddle vessels. One of the latter type, with a low-pressure cylinder of 112 in. bore, developed 9,000 hp. As a plain horizontal type it was readily adapted for compound or triple expansion working with a wide variety of cylinder and crank arrangements for mill drives up to 4,000 hp, and for metal-rolling mills as much as 12,000 hp was developed by coupling three cylinders to one crankshaft. It was the most persistent type of steam engine for mill driving, from Trevithick in 1803 (Fig. 12) to the last mill engine, a uniflow built in 1937.

Inverted Vertical 1845 In this type (see Fig. 15) the cylinder was overhead, driving downwards to the crankshaft beneath it, and from Nasmyth's steam-hammer engine of 1845 it was adopted for driving screw propellers in vessels in the 1850s and for mill drive in 1874 when a large engine of this type was installed in a textile mill in Bolton. It was very popular for small powers, many thousands being made for driving small workshops all over the world, as when combined with a vertical boiler they were comparatively cheap to purchase, install, and operate. They became widely used in textile mills, with two or three crank arrangements developing up to 3,500 hp, while some used in rolling mills developed 18,000 hp on three cranks. A small number of engines were built with a horizontal and a vertical cylinder connected to the same crankpin: these were known as 'Manhattan engines' and were designed for very high powers in Britain and the U.S.A. up to 1914.

High Speed from 1862 Most of the designs outlined so far were of the slow speed type, running at speeds up to 100 rpm, with 55–60 rpm being normal for the larger sizes, while beam mill engines and engines in paddle steamers ran at up to 40 rpm. The locomotive engine had long led in the field of increasing speeds and steam pressures, and by 1860 these were working with steam pressures of 120 psi at 300 rpm in everyday service. However, despite the obvious advantages of such speeds, they had little effect upon stationary engine design, where massive condensing engines remained the standard practice. The first recognition of the value of higher speeds in stationary engines came in the 1860s, when Charles T. Porter, who was then making a very efficient high-speed governor, met J. F. Allen, who had designed a double-acting engine to run at a speed of 150 rpm incorporating separate inlet and exhaust valves with governor-controlled cut-off. As a result of this meeting the first of Allen's engines was displayed at the London Exhibition of 1862, running perfectly at the remarkable speed of 150 rpm even though the authorities had specified a limit of 120 rpm. It was run non-condensing, as indeed were most American engines at the time, and this together with the high speed was so novel for stationary duties that it was distrusted and made little immediate impact in Britain, although it was sold at the last minute to Easton & Amos, who used it to drive a cupola blower in their foundry. But opinion changed gradually in Britain, and in the 1870s several designs of single-acting engines appeared which were totally enclosed and ran at up to 300 rpm. By 1874, P. W. Willans had made at Penns Works the first of the high-speed engines which were to bring him widespread fame. Other high-speed engines were invented about this time by Halsey, Wigzell, Vosper, and Brotherhood, but apart from the Willans only the Brotherhood type made a major impact. This became much used as an auxiliary engine, but its main application has been as a propelling unit for torpedoes, since its radial layout, with the cylinders arranged around the crank-shaft, made it very compact. Driven by compressed air, it has been, and still is, more widely used than any early single-acting design. The Willans engine, meanwhile, made a great contribution to the development of the electricity-generating industry, several thousands being made up to about 1910, most of them directly connected to generators, and some of them being still in use in the 1950s. Of the 102,000 hp generated in British electricity stations in 1895, no less than 53,000 hp was produced by Willans engines. Their success was due partly to the fact that the inventor was a superb engineer who developed his design to give high economy, and partly to the extremely accurate production techniques with one of the best systems of precision gauging of the period. The special feature of the later Willans engines was that there was a complete engine to each crank, with two or three cylinders arranged in line, according to whether they were com-pound or triple expansion, above each crank. The piston valves were in a trunk inside the main pistons, and were operated by eccentrics which were forged solidly with the crankpins. The construction can be seen in a sectioned engine in the London Science Museum. Despite the success of the Willans engine, however, it was becoming obvious in the 1890s that the growth of the public electricity-supply industry would soon outstrip the capacity of the reciprocating steam engine, so that it began to be replaced by the steam turbine with its higher capacity per unit and greatly reduced vibration.

High Speed – Forced Lubrication from 1890 One innovation which has influenced the later development of steam-engine design and has done more than any other single factor to maintain the competitiveness of the reciprocating steam engine, was the introduction of the system of forced lubrication applied to high-speed engines invented by A. C. Paine in 1890–92. In this design the working parts are enclosed within a casing and lubricated with oil at low pressure through drilled ports. It was a brilliant idea and was developed with great success by Belliss & Morcom. Thousands of these engines were built, mainly for electricity generating, although a small number were used for driving waterworks pumps as well as a few mill units with rope or belt drive. Besides being very reliable and requiring no attention when running, so that they could be readily adapted for small power loads, they were valuable in services which required heat as well as power, such as the paper and textile finishing trades, where the engines provided the power and the exhaust supplied the heat. Very few horizontal engines of this type were made in Britain, but verticals were made by several manufacturers working on simple, compound and triple expansion cycles, sometimes with tandem cylinders, and up to 3,000 hp. They were termed 'quick-revolution engines' by Belliss & Morcom, who built a very large number of them during the period of the patent and continued to do so until the demand fell off in the 1960s. Their first engine of this type is preserved in the London Science Museum.

Uniflow _c._ 1900 In the uniflow engine the steam moved in one direction only, entering at the end of the cylinder and exhausting at a ring of ports in the middle of the barrel (see Fig. 16). Developed at the turn of the present century by Professor J. Stumpf of Berlin, as a logical application of theory to design, it was the last major development of the reciprocating steam engine. It was not a new idea, however, as it had been first used by J. Perkins in 1827, patented by Eaton in the U.S.A. in the 1850s, and again by L. J. Todd of London in the 1880s. It certainly fulfilled the intentions of the design in reducing heat losses within the cylinder, a characteristic which was particularly valuable where there were long periods of light load when cylinder condensation became a serious disadvantage with the usual counterflow cycle. Despite the apparent simplicity of the design, stresses and thermal effects caused many troubles to develop, but it was a very economical type, and at least one ran for nearly sixty years without the cylinder being rebored. This sort of economy led to its extensive use in many industries, but only in the U.S.A. was it widely used in marine service. Once it had proved to be a practical and economical engine, manufacture was taken up widely in Europe, and continued for some thirty years until the demand for slow-speed steam engines disappeared. Coming so late in the history of the steam engine, when the competition of other power sources was great, its impact varied. Some makers built only one or two, while one British manufacturer built as many as sixty.

Steam Turbine from 1884 The steam turbine produces a rotative effort directly from the steam to the shaft without the intervention of reciprocating motion. This was an idea which haunted designers from the beginning of steam power, and there was much intermittent discussion of a philosophical nature regarding the assumed loss of power by the crank and flywheel mechanism and the reversal of movements at every revolution. Many attempts were made to secure rotating motion from a vane or piston attached to the shaft, upon which the steam could act directly, from James Watt onwards. Almost every conceivable combination of shapes, packings, and moving abutments, was tried out, but all failed either from excessive friction if they were made steam-tight, or from leakage if they were not, or else from damage as sliding vanes made contact with other parts. The breakthrough came with the turbine which uses the energy in the steam by expanding it in nozzles to give high velocities, and then converting it into work by passing it across curved vanes set in the periphery of wheels, thus avoiding the difficulties of mechanical contacts, leakage and friction. In this way the steam turbine made possible

the use of higher pressures and temperatures which, by extend-
ing the range of the heat drop within the cycle, now achieves
thermal efficiencies which were until recently no more than
philosophers' dreams.

The steam turbine was developed at a time when higher speeds
and powers were urgently required for the generation of electricity and for marine services. The first practical turbines of
Charles Parsons (1884), who adopted the reaction system, and
de Laval (1889), who utilized the impulse effect of steam expanding in a nozzle, were of fairly low power. Parsons, however, soon
developed designs giving speeds suitable for direct connection to
generators in everyday use, although the de Laval type had to
run at very high speeds since all of the energy was produced in
a single stage and so drove through gearing of about 10–1 ratio
with a maximum of some 500 hp. These limitations soon led to
the invention of impulse turbines with the expansion of the steam
split into many stages, giving efficiency at lower speeds. The turbine has made possible the greatest development of the steam
prime mover, from Parsons's 10 hp unit of 1884 to the giant
turbo-alternators of today which develop some 600,000 hp at a
fraction of the fuel consumption of earlier steam engines. Fig. 17
illustrates the de Laval, the simplest of all steam turbines. The
steam enters by the pipe, and passes through the nozzle SN,
the diverging bore of which converts its pressure energy into
velocity, the jet emerging at velocities approaching 4,000 feet
per second. This is converted into useful effort by passing it
across the curved blades BDS upon the rim of the wheel W delivering the power through the shaft S. The spent steam then
passes into the casing CSG surrounding the wheel to pass to the
surface condenser SFC by the exhaust pipe X. The condenser
contains numerous tubes CT containing the cooling water, and
the condensed water and air are extracted by the air-pump AP
to complete the cycle.

CHAPTER FIVE

Constructional Details

INTRODUCTION

Although the broad mechanical principles outlined in the previous
chapter applied to steam engines in general, there was an extremely wide range of variations in the construction of the individual parts, and the developments in the finish of these details
were in many cases the story of the evolution of machine tools.
A piston working within a cylinder required a flexible structure
which would allow the piston to slide, yet prevent steam from
leaking from one side to the other, and with the exception of the
smallest engines adjustments for wear had to be provided wherever one part worked upon another, such as the eccentrics and
the ends of the connecting rod and other moving parts. Valves
were also needed in order to admit and release the steam from
the cylinder. There were different ways of meeting all these
needs, so that the opportunities for variety in constructional
details of engines were almost endless.

The facilities for construction also influenced design. Thus the
early engines contained a maximum of the timber and stone
which were available locally together with the craftsmen to work
them, and a minimum of metal work. As cast iron became more
readily available, however, the art of metal founding was employed more and more in the construction of steam engines, so
that by the beginning of the nineteenth century many engines
were made almost entirely of cast iron, and since few metals but
cast iron will work well in contact with each other it was usual
to fit easily adjustable bearings, generally of bronze (although
they were frequently described as 'brasses'), to the forged ends
where parts rubbed together in working. The granular structure
of cast iron made it necessary to use it with care, so that stresses
were applied with a minimum of tension or bending and, together
with the desire that it should look right, this led to delightfully
light and ornate forms in the engine beams, framing, and connecting rods.

Although it appeared to be sheer ornament, much of this work was often skilled design of a very high order, and this should be considered when studying an early engine constructed largely of cast iron. The circle, a strong form, was often incorporated, together with gentle curves, to effect necessary changes of direction in stresses, so that a vertical part taking lateral stresses was enabled to transfer them to a stiff horizontal base without tension or bending which might have caused failure in the brittle cast iron. It is only when considered in this light that the subtlety and skill of the early designers becomes evident, and that their curves, arabesques, and mouldings can be appreciated as part of the technical and structural artistry of the work as well as its visual attraction. The early cruciform cast-iron connecting rods were both elegant and scientific in the use of material, and the same was true of many cast-iron engine beds and entablatures.

With every care in construction, it was necessary to subject some cast-iron parts to alternating stresses, and particular attention was given to the crankshaft, which, when made of ample size and with high-quality material, in many cases gave a century of service (say, 140 million alternations of stress) without failing. Because of its granular nature, however, cast iron was always liable to fail either from fatigue or from hidden blowholes in the castings themselves, and as tough wrought iron became available in substantial masses its use became widespread in steam engines, so that the smith and the foundryman shared the business of engine building more evenly than hitherto. This development led to the incorporation of delightful curvatures and bosses raised from the solid metal in the middle of links and levers, and as steel also became a major constructional material these features were found more and more frequently in steam engines. But cast iron remained the material of the greater part of the engine structure: the cylinders, beds, and flywheels were almost always cast, with only the highly stressed moving parts made from forgings of wrought iron or steel, as these were considerably more costly to produce. The predominance of cast iron was due to its ability to follow the form of the patterns ('moulds') and so to be readily made in the strongest shapes, and also to its ability to work satisfactorily with almost every metal, including itself.

Full descriptions of the illustrations are to be found in the Gazetteer on page 175.

1.   Kew Bridge Pumping Station (Metropolitan Water Board)

2. Springhead Pumping Station (Hull Waterworks)

3. Papplewick Pumping Station (Nottingham Waterworks)

4. Roall Pumping Station (The Pontefract, Goole and Selby Water Board)

5. Lound Pumping Station (Lowestoft Water Works)

6. *Below* Crossness Pumping Station (London Main Drainage System)

7. *Above right* Coleham Sewage Pumping Station (Shrewsbury)

8. *Below right* Abbey Lane Sewage Pumping Station (City of Leicester)

9. Cheddars Lane Sewage Pumping Station (City of Cambridge)

10. *Right* Stretham Pumping Station (The Waterbeach Drainage Level, Ely)

11. Curry Moor Pumping Station (The Somerset Rivers Drainage Board)

12. Engine of PS *Leven* (Dumbarton)

13. Engines of PS *Clyde* (Renfrew Ferry Landing)

14. Engines of PS *Empress* (The Maritime Museum, Southampton)

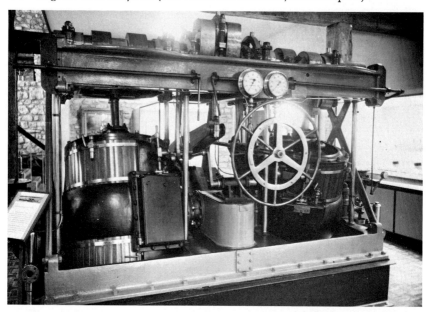

15. Henwood Pumping Station (Ashford Waterworks, Kent)

16. Morton Colliery Engine, Derbyshire (Leicester Civic Museum)

17. Fieldhouse Brickworks Engine (Tolson Museum, Huddersfield)

18. Baggs' Brewery Engine, Kings Lynn (The Bridewell Museum, Norwich)

19. Small Oscillating Engines (The Bridewell Museum, Norwich)

20. Weaving Shed Engine (Near India Mill, Darwen, Lancashire)

21. White's Tannery Engine (The Bradford Industrial Museum, Yorkshire)

22. Courtaulds' Dee Mill Engine (Shaw, near Oldham, Lancashire)

23. Carbolite Mill Engine (Bamford, Derbyshire)

THE ENGINE HOUSE

The first engines, employed as mine pumps in the eighteenth century, were almost literally 'house-built' in that the main structural members were massive timbers which were actually part of the building, the stresses being largely downwards. This house-built principle survived as long as beam engines were built – i.e. into the early twentieth century – although not all beam engines, of course, employed it. The principle was considerably modified with the introduction of rotative engines for the mills, since in these the stresses were reversed at each revolution, and they also required a massive foundation to keep the parts in alignment. In such mill engines the upper part of the engine framing was frequently built into the engine house, but even so the main stress was taken by the foundation, which, usually of dressed ashlar stone and often 20 feet deep, weighing many tons, maintained the alignment of the engine by its sheer weight and solidity.

It was soon found advantageous, however, to place a rigid metal bedplate upon the top of the stone foundations, with the metal parts of the engine attached to it, and this procedure lasted for as long as steam engines were built for heavy duties. The engine house was influenced by this, as it now became more of a massive foundation to which the engine itself was attached, surrounded by a protective shell to which an immense range of decorative schemes was applied. In the large-beam engine houses of the early period, the walls were usually plastered and then finished with decorative lining schemes, the wall paint being usually light in colour to add brightness, as many single-beam engine houses were long and narrow structures. The railings around the crank pits and upon the upper platforms (the working parts were even then customarily protected by railings) were often decorative and, here again, neat painting added to the attractiveness. It was customary for an engine-building concern to adopt a specific type of cast-iron railing design which, since they were usually of a standard size, were a stock foundry job, to be fitted into odd spaces in the moulding boxes. Another feature was to finish the beam-supporting columns with imitation marble graining, and one large pair of engines by Petrie of Rochdale were outstanding for this and for the carpets which were laid on the engine-room floor. Protective walking ways of linoleum were frequently found in engine rooms, with the open spaces

D

finely finished with whiting. The large mill engine houses were certainly made highly attractive when the management and the engineer were prepared to provide the material and the effort. For the smaller engine rooms, where such cost could not be met, simple trackways of carding flats sufficed for walking ways, but many small early beam engines simply had the flagstone floor with only plastered and painted walls.

For many years in the development of the mill steam engine, the engine was housed within the main mill structure, and was easily identified by the characteristic tall windows of the beam-engine house, sometimes being placed at the end but often in the middle of the mill length. The latter arrangement was very convenient where the mill was driven by gearing and a vertical shaft, since an upright shaft could be placed so as to drive the horizontal shafts on the mill floors by simple bevel gearing, and by placing the engine and vertical shaft in the centre of the building the horizontal shafts could be made shorter and were thus subject to less strain. In some cases, as a mill grew, each extension became a separate unit and acquired its own engine and drives. In later years, as engines became more economical, it became the practice to place one large engine in the mill yard and to couple other blocks of the mill to this by shafting or ropes, which led to some complex but effective engineering arrangements.

Gearing was usually noisy, and in the 1860s main drives by belts or ropes were introduced, and these again affected the engine room, since such drives required considerable length between the shaft centres to work at their best. As the main mill room shafts were still in the same position, this meant that the engine had to be farther away, so that it became normal practice to house the engine outside the main body of the mill, thus creating the layout which became standard all over the world as long as steam-engine main drives remained in use. The proportioning and finishing of the engine room in relation to the mill exterior engaged the sympathetic attention of owners and their architects and produced in the Lancashire cotton-spinning mills some of the finest functional buildings in the country. The stone-built mills so characteristic of Yorkshire also on occasion achieved grandiose proportions, their very soundness and permanence enabling them to acquire a weathered exterior, although the final effect, as at Dalton Mills, Keighley, or Listers at Bradford or Salts Mill at Saltaire, was frequently charming as well as impressive. Such structures bred men who were equally staunch and, all too frequently, as difficult to deal with as the structure of the mill itself.

The shape of the engine room naturally varied with the type of the engine, so that a single crank beam or tandem engine room was long and narrow whilst the double crank engines were usually housed in a room which was more nearly square. Changes in the engines often influenced the engine room as a mill developed, and when some single-cylinder horizontal engines were converted into tandem compound, the engine room had to be extended to take the added cylinder. In one mill in Bolton this required 15 feet to be built out from the mill structure, and when a mill was changed from gear to rope driving, a complete new engine room was often built to give the length for the rope drive.

As the practice developed of preparing a separate cast-iron bedplate upon which all the main parts of the engine were fitted, the amount of work necessary to install an engine was reduced, since the alignment was done in the workshop rather than in the engine house, the prime need on the site being a massive flat-topped masonry bed. Plate 21 illustrates this type of simple box-section casting upon which the engine parts were fitted. Such beds could be made with very limited equipment, although they still involved a great deal of hand work by the fitters, but as the nineteenth century progressed, so did the machine tools which not only increased in accuracy but also in capacity. It thus became the practice to design the engine in such a way that most of the accurately fitting surfaces were produced by machine tools. This included the engine beds, in which the crosshead guiding system was often made circular so that the crosshead and guides were produced by machine and the faces for the cylinder were finished in the same machine at one setting. Plate 23 illustrates a bed of this type, which was used for the largest engines. Sometimes, although the bed was still a box section, the crosshead surfaces were planed flat, permitting larger bearing surfaces to be provided, as shown in Plate 20.

CONNECTING RODS, CRANKS, AND FLYWHEELS

Connecting Rods Since the ends of the connecting rod had very different motions, one rectilinear and the other rotative, the wear and the stresses upon them were unequal. Different types of bearing were thus frequently used in one rod. The crankpin bearing, often termed the 'big end', was of four main types:

1. The earliest was the 'foundry' type, which was a box cast upon the end of the cast-iron rod, into which the bearings or 'brasses' were fitted. It required a lot of hand fitting but was strong and readily made without machine tools. Plate 18 shows this type, which was frequently made attractive by decorative moulding upon the foot, which was sometimes raised at the edges or comprised a simple fluted motif.

2. Another early design was a simple forged wrought-iron strap, fitting upon a rectangular boss forged on the end of the rod, which held the brasses, the strap being secured by cotters which were also used to adjust the brasses when they were worn. Like the foundry type, this was largely a matter of hand-work, being forged by the smith and finished by the fitter. It is illustrated in Fig. 13.

3. As machine tools developed, it became customary to forge the connecting rods instead of casting them, and with this an end similar to the foundry type was used in which a massive box was forged and the space for the brasses was cut out and largely finished by slotting and shaping machines. As with the foundry type, the brasses were held and adjusted by cotters. This type is shown in Fig. 14, and also in Plate 12.

4. The solid or box ends could only be used with an overhung crank (Figs. 14 and 16) – that is, where the rod could be fitted sideways over the pin – but for marine service, and where it was necessary to have two or three cranks per engine with the drive off one end, cranks had to have double webs, and the marine type of end was used for this. The connecting rod was forged with a flat on the end, and the brasses were held together by two massive bolts which also had a heavy flat plate to keep the brasses in place. It could be easily finished by hand or machine, and was used for all types of engine. It is shown in Figs. 15 and 16, and also in Plate 14.

These descriptions apply equally to the ends of all motion rods, including the eccentric and valve driving rods, but for the small engines plain bushes were often fitted.

Crosshead Guides The need for the piston and rod to work in a straight line is evident, and was met at first by parallel motions in various arrangements which continued to be used extensively for as long as beam engines were made, and later by the system of crosshead and guides. The main requirement was that the surfaces should be flat and in line, but in the case of reversing engines the guides had also to provide for the loading to be reversed when the engine changed direction. There were several ways of achieving this:

1. The 'four-bar' type, which provided an equal surface for the top and bottom of the crosshead (see Plate 21) and allowed ample wearing surface as wear could be taken up by packing the slide bars. Since the parts were small they could be prepared by hand.

2. The 'trunk' guide was circular in section, with the bearing surface bored inside and with a turned circular guiding surface on the crosshead. This was produced by machine tools and was widely used in later years of steam-engine service for both open types and for forced-lubrication engines. It was adopted for all uses except marine engines and locomotives. This type is illustrated in Plate 23.

3. The 'slipper' guide was rectangular and flat at the bottom, working upon a flat surface planed on the engine bed. It was extensively adopted where reversing was infrequent, being provided with only a limited area for the upper side. It had the great advantage of leaving the front of the engine open and accessible, and was widely used for marine service.

4. The 'Laird' or box-section crosshead required only a single rectangular slide bar, as the crosshead wrapped it on all four sides. The wearing surface could be made ample, although possibly it was weak at the centre. It was extensively used for locomotives and for small marine engines.

Cranks and Crankshafts These converted the thrust of the piston into rotary motion. In the early engines the shaft was frequently square and of cast iron, with turned parts only for the bearings, and such cast-iron shafts could be up to 32 inches across in the centre, where the flywheel fitted. Wrought iron and later steel were used as they became available, since cast iron was brittle and could give trouble if there were blow-holes or other weaknesses. The flywheel was usually fitted by staking on – that is, flats were accurately prepared upon four or six sides of the boss and shaft, but with a space between them in which the stakes, which were massive flat keys, were fitted with extreme accuracy. Since the stakes had to transmit the power of the engine, they had to fit solidly and fully all the way in the flywheel boss and upon the shaft, parts which often weighed several tons each, and the bedding of the stakes by scraping was both highly skilled and arduous, as each stake had to be driven up and bedded little by little until it was in place. Such was the accuracy achieved, however, that many flywheels so fitted frequently transmitted up to 3,000 hp for many years without needing attention.

The crankshaft was either a plain forging with a crank fitted at one or both ends, or else the cranks were forged from the ingot, and sometimes were cut out rather than forged. Smaller crankshafts, particularly for pumps, were often forged from a single circular bar, only turned for the bearings (Fig. 15 illustrates this type). Cranks ranged widely in design. The early cranks were of cast iron, often with the metal scientifically distributed for maximum strength, with a web of 'U' or 'T' section, and frequently with ornamental moulding. Many such cranks gave over half a century of service. The 'disc' crank (Fig. 14) was also usually of cast metal, frequently combining a balance weight in the disc to counterbalance the weight of the connecting rod: they very rarely failed in service, but some later ones were made of cast steel. Most cranks, however, were iron or steel forgings, many makers having a characteristic boss and curve design for the web, which helps to identify them. Thus Pollit & Wigzells almost always finished their cranks in the lathe, with radiused sides which provided a distinctive mark to their engines. Most mill-engine cranks were shrunk on, the eye being bored small and the crank fitted by heating it and putting it on the shaft when hot, the ensuing shrinkage giving a grip that rarely failed.

Flywheels The flywheel was often the heaviest part of an engine, weighing anything from a few hundredweights in a small engine to 120 tons for a 3,000 hp mill engine, or even more for a continuous-sheet rolling mill, some of which were as much as 160 tons. Small flywheels, up to 5 feet in diameter, were frequently cast in one piece, with the hub bored to fit the crankshaft, and held by a key and keyway. Since such flywheels originated as molten metal at high temperature there was contraction as it cooled which, even with the greatest care, left stresses in the structure as the rim contracted more than the boss. For larger wheels this difficulty was avoided by making them in halves held together by bolts, often with hoops shrunk on to the boss. With even larger wheels, of 12 feet diameter or more, the practice from Watt onwards was to assemble the flywheel from separate castings for the hub, the arms, and the rim in sectors, usually with half-lapped joints bolted together. The surfaces were chipped and filed, but frequently with square sockets in the rim sectors with forged square keys cottered in. The very heavy flywheels of the early rolling mills were usually made without any machine or hand finishing by casting the parts as male and female dovetails with a large clearance between them. These spaces were then filled with hardwood wedges, and as these shrank they were tightened by driving steel wedges into the timber packing. This method was adopted for all of the gear as well as the flywheel parts, resulting in surprising accuracy and durability as well as a valuable amount of resilience.

The large textile-mill flywheels were customarily run as fast as safety permitted, with the drive taken by round cotton ropes running in grooves turned in the rim. The peripheral speed sometimes reached 5,000 feet per minute, when a single large rope 2 inches in diameter would transmit 50 hp. Such wheels needed to be very accurately built, and were made with the boss, arms, and rim sectors as separate castings, machined and hand-scraped wherever they fitted together. The arms were fitted into taper sockets in the boss, and were held in slots in the boss and the arms by flat cotters which were scraped to a continuous metallic contact at all points. Unless this was well done, trouble soon developed as the rim pulled on them. This, however, was exceptionally rare, and many flywheels made in this way ran for half a century untouched. The largest wheels often consisted of two wheels side by side, and the widest of all, installed at the Pear Mill, Bredbury, which had grooves for 73 ropes, contained three separate wheels set closely together on the shaft, and that certainly ran for fifty years without attention. Such hand-finished fitting was the peak of the engineer's craft. The continental-type flywheels were usually bored to fit and keyed, and Scott & Hodgsons did this in Britain using twin tangential keys.

Driving from the flywheel was often achieved by toothed gearing, and this involved a gear ring on pads faced upon the arms, or a separate wheel staked upon the crankshaft, or by Fairbairn's method of teeth upon the rim of the flywheel, which were later separate sectors fitted into dovetails in the rim and wedged. It was customary to keep the tooth speed down below 2,000 feet per minute, and it was found that shorter teeth were stronger than the usual forms.

Driving by belt from the flywheel was introduced for textile-mill main drives about 1870, and although this method was not extensively adopted, it was very quiet. But round ropes were cheaper and, being introduced about the same time, soon became standard for large mills. There was a return to driving by belts in 1912, when a number of mills were fitted with steel belts. Although most of these were later converted to ropes, at least two steel belt drives were used for over forty years. They ran upon steel faces fitted to the rim and faced with cork.

CYLINDERS, PISTONS AND VALVES

These were the most important elements in the steam engine and were usually made of cast iron throughout, since it works well with other cast-iron parts.

Cylinders In the Newcomen engine this was a plain circular tube, with all the fittings attached to the bottom (Fig. 9). The bore had to be as smooth as possible in all cylinders, and until Wilkinson patented his boring machine in the 1770s this was only achieved with great difficulty by dragging moulded lead sections coated with grinding material to and fro in the cylinder. It was customary in the early days of steam-engine manufacture to make the cylinder as a plain tube, with ports or nozzles at the top and bottom to which the chambers containing the valves were attached, and this remained for long the practice with all large cylinders. This enabled the valve systems not only to be made separately, but also to be varied later in use as they were readily detached. With the development of the locomotive and small factory engines, having a single sliding valve to control all the steam events, the practice was adopted of casting the valve chest and ports in one with the cylinder, and as the art of casting grew and the knowledge of the stresses that were involved became more fully understood, cylinder castings became very complex structures which included the chambers for the four valves necessary for the steam events, and numerous bosses for the attachment of the fittings. Certainly the foundryman needed to be a very highly skilled craftsman to cast the later cylinders, where all four valves were placed close together at the cylinder ends (as in Plate 20), for in such a casting as many as forty 'cores' (solid parts inserted in the casting to produce apertures for the steam passages and valve chambers) were required. The Watt engine had its simple valve boxes attached to rectangular flanged ports at the top and bottom of the cylinder, but this was sometimes simplified by making the lower port in the bottom casting upon which the cylinder stood. Since the cylinder was cast from molten metal, it contracted considerably upon solidifying, which locked stresses within the metal. This had to be taken into account in the design if the brittle castings were not to fracture in machining or in service. Mixing irons from various furnaces sometimes aided the foundryman by modifying the quality of the metal, but the need for very hard working surfaces for the bore had always to be remembered. Such glass-hard surfaces were necessary for the long life of the engine, but they presented great problems both to the moulder, because the metal was so very brittle, and to the man who bored them to a smooth interior, whose tools were sorely tried since it was usual to complete each cut without stopping to avoid ridging the surface. With the development of the Corliss and drop valves, needing circular ports in which to work, the practice was to cast the ports and seats in one with the cylinder, and again some of the largest of these cylinders were foundry masterpieces. Improved machine tools allowed all the faces of the cylinder to be machined in one setting, which was a great advantage. In the later engines the valve ports were cast in a separate casting for each end, or else in one with the cylinder head. This reduced the risk of failure in a complex and costly casting, and placing the valves in the heads also reduced the clearance space at the end of the stroke.

It was usual to cast the cylinder fixing lugs with the cylinder barrel. The ends were closed by covers held on by rings of studs or bolts, and these were simple castings with bosses for the packing needed for the piston rod. The early packing was hemp rope compressed around the moving rod, and for nearly a century various fabrics were used for this, but with the re-introduction of metallic packing for the rods the advantages were such that these soon became a standard fitting. We say 're-introduction' because Cartwright and others had proposed such materials as early as 1797, but it was the type of metallic packing developed in the United States in the 1880s which was adopted in most subsequent steam engines. Even so, 'soft' packings of fabric have always been widely used and still are used for smaller-sized rods. They have improved greatly in quality over the years.

Pistons These were discs turned to fit the cylinder with a minimum of clearance, and with provision for packing rings in the edges, to prevent leakage around the clearance. The packing rings were made with every conceivable arrangement of springs and adjustments in later years, and the piston was frequently made with a removable cover to allow access to the rings without removal of the piston from the cylinder. This retained the name 'junk ring' from the days when the pistons for early low-pressure steam engines were indeed packed with junk or old rope saturated with tallow and compressed by the ring and the bolts which held it. This tended to fail or required much attention as the temperature of the steam increased, and metal rings were adopted as early as 1845 by Penns for warship screw engines after a great number of designs had been tried ashore. The problem of maintaining a sliding steam-tight fit for the piston was certainly a difficult one, and countless variations were tried to solve it, but none proved perfect. In the end, as so often, the simplest was probably the best, and the simple Ramsbottom spring rings, made to give a slight pressure on the cylinder walls with or without steam pressure behind them, gave as good service to the thousands of steam engines fitted with them as they do now in the millions of oil and petrol engines fitted with them over a century after they were introduced.

Valves Valves were necessary to admit the steam in order to act upon the piston, and to release it after the work had been performed, so that they were a most important detail in the design of an engine. They worked upon three broad principles: viz. – they could be rotated upon a curved seat; they could slide upon a flat seat; or they could be simply discs which were raised and dropped upon ports in the cylinder. There were many variants upon these basic forms, so it will be useful to trace the main steps in the evolution of steam valves.

Plug Cock (Savery, 1698) This was the common faucet, consisting of a tapered plug with a hole across the centre which fitted into and could turn within a body containing holes to match those in the plug. The control was by turning the plug so that the hole or the blank part aligned with the hole in the body. It was a simple mechanism, familiar to local craftsmen, and was well suited to Savery's engine, in which the movement of the steam was gradual.

Flat Swinging Valve (Newcomen, 1712) Cocks of large size were clumsy and difficult to operate, and were unsuitable for the Newcomen engine, in which large volumes of steam at low pressure had to move into the cylinder rapidly. This requirement led to the use of a valve which was a simple flat plate placed inside the boiler so that it opened and closed the end of the steam pipe from the boiler by swinging across it. Thus the only working steam joint was for the spindle which operated the flat plate sector. It was readily made by the craftsmen of the period and was suitable for the Newcomen engine, which only needed a single steam valve that could be worked by a simple linkage.

Lifting Valve with Conical Seats (Watt, 1769) Watt's engine, with its separate condenser, higher steam pressure, and the need to admit and exhaust steam from each end of the cylinder independently, required a more sophisticated mechanism than that employed on the Newcomen engine. He adopted flat circular lifting valves with tapered edges which fitted into, and were ground in to match, similar seats in the valve chest, lifting and dropping vertically upon the port transferring the steam. The valves and the seats were made of brass, and the latter were separate from and held in place by the valve chest castings in Watt's engines. Watt recognized the need for the valves to open and close rapidly, and although it must have been noisy he arranged for the valves to operate quickly. Knowing the value of expanding the steam in the cylinder, Watt patented expansive working in 1782, and soon designed his engines to work with the steam cut-off at a part of the stroke. Unfortunately, his customers found that they could obtain more power by admitting steam through all the stroke and altered their engines to do this, but since the boilers were designed to provide steam for only part of a stroke they were unable to give sufficient steam for full-stroke working. This caused many complaints which led Watt to abandon the practice of expansion.

Slide Valve (Murdock, 1785) The increasing use of steam engines for smaller works, even as low as 2 or 4 hp, and the general need to simplify engines, led to efforts to combine several valve functions in a single part. Watt's brilliant assistant Murdock was probably the first to do this in his oscillating cylinder engine of 1785. In this, the valve was of square section, working within a square chamber at the side of the cylinder. By hollowing out the centre part of the valve Murdock was able to arrange for admission at the centre, with the exhaust taking place over the ends. It is interesting to note that the theme of a square valve working in a square chamber was revived about a century later as the Valley Automatic engine in the U.S.A.

The Long 'D' Valve (Murdock, 1799) It was Murdock who made the single valve generally applicable when he invented the long 'D' valve in 1799. This was a tube of 'D' section, with enlarged ends, which worked in a channel of similar section at the side of the cylinder. The flat side of the 'D' worked upon a face and ports on the side at each end of the cylinder, with a tubular connection between the two end 'D' valves. The round back of the moving tube was made steam-tight by hemp packing fitted into a groove at each end of the valve, and moving with it. This type of valve was regularly used even for the largest marine paddle engines on the Atlantic run into the 1860s, but one improvement in the later valves was that the packing was placed in a chamber in the valve chest, and was adjusted by a cover which could be tightened to compress it on the round back of the valve-ends.

The Short 'D' Valve (Murray, 1802) With the ending of Watt's patent in 1800, many developments occurred to make the steam engine more widely usable, and amongst these was the short 'D' valve introduced by Matthew Murray. This was simply a hollow cast-iron box with flat faces which were ground to be steam-tight with the valve chest face on which it moved to and fro (Fig. 18). It alternately opened the ports at each end of the cylinder to admit steam from the chest and then, as it moved, allowed the transfer of the used steam to the inside of the box and thus to the exhaust pipe. It was the simplest mechanism that could be devised to perform the functions, and was self-adjusting by the pressure on the back and only needed a single reciprocating valve rod to operate it. There were many modfications later to allow it to work at increasing steam pressures, some of which were relief frames which removed the pressure from a part of the back of the valve. Sometimes an additional valve was fitted upon the back of the main valve to allow variation in the point at which the steam was cut off, or a valve was fitted on the back of the valve chest to cut off the steam from the chest. If the valve was the same length as the ports, steam was admitted for the entire stroke, but with its virtually standard use on locomotives, with link reversing motion, it was possible to cut off the steam at any part of the stroke by adding lap to the valve and varying the travel. 'Lap' consisted of making the slide valve longer than the overall length of the steam ports, so that the steam was cut off before the valve reached the end of its travel. This was also done with stationary engines, but since these did not reverse it was customary to use a single eccentric while retaining the link and variable travel. The most widely used back cut-off valves were the Meyer and the Rider. Another method of varying the cut-off point was the use of a separate drop valve which was placed at the inlet to the valve chest, and was opened at every stroke of the engine. This was adopted very early by Watt (see the Watt engine in the Science Museum) and was used on the large Atlantic paddle vessels in the 1860s. The drop cut-off valve was also developed late in the nineteenth century by Kuhn, Nordberg and others to work under governor control, as an auxiliary that could be fitted to existing engines in various services.

Piston Valve (from the 1820s) In a way the logical development of the 'D' valve, the piston valve consists of a circular bobbin working in a bored chamber at each end of the cylinder, with the two bobbins connected by a rod (Fig. 19). As each bobbin moved to and fro, it exposed the port in the cylinder alternately to the steam or the exhaust connections. It had many advantages, since being turned and bored it could be conveniently made by rotating tools: it worked with little friction, and steam-tightness was ensured by fitting metal rings to the bobbins which were more durable than the hemp packings of the 'D' type. It was as widely used as the slide valve, each being applied to every service for which the steam engine was used. A similar design was used by Trevithick for his water-pressure engines, in which the valves were plugs of lead cast into the tubular channel or valve chest, before it was adopted for steam engines. There were two variants

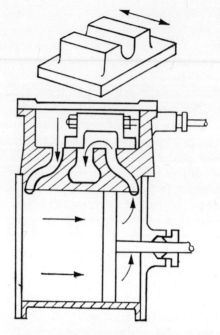

Figure 18   Slide valve

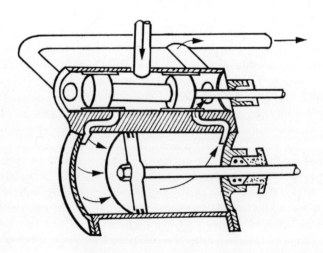

Figure 19   Piston valve

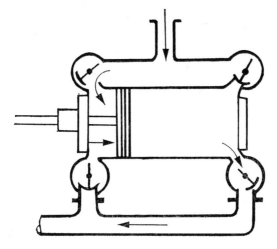

Figure 20   Corliss valve

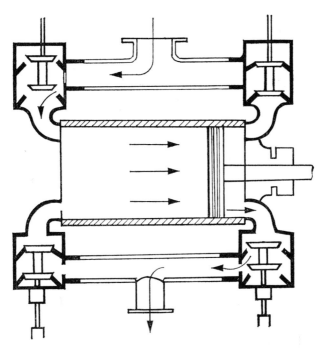

Figure 21   Equilibrium drop valve

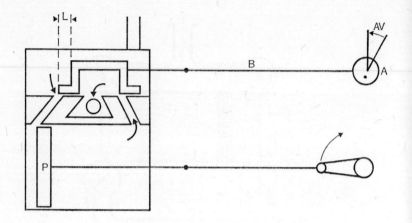

Figure 22   Valve gear: slide valves

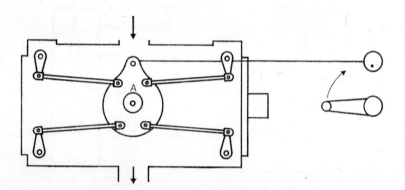

Figure 23   Valve gear: independent control

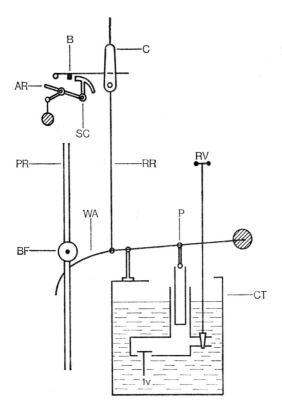

Figure 24   Cornish cycle: the cataract

of the plain circular bobbin valve. In one, the 'twist piston valve', the valve was made to twist about ten degrees at each stroke, to even the wear on the valve and the liner. In the other variant, the 'internal cut-off valve', the valve was made as a ported tube, inside which another valve worked, each having independent movements to allow inside variations in the steam cut-off point.

Corliss Valve (from 1849) Slide valves had several disadvantages, and as steam pressures increased, these became more apparent. Besides being heavy to operate and not easy to maintain in steam-tight condition they had other drawbacks: the steam had to enter the cylinder and leave it by the same passage, the friction was considerable, and so was the volume of the clearance or dead spaces at the end of the cylinder. The Corliss valve was designed to relieve these disadvantages (Figs. 14 and 20). It consisted of a separate steam and exhaust valve for each end of the cylinder, with each valve having an arm which rocked or half-rotated it upon a bored face containing the port. As the valves were small and the areas in contact very limited, the friction was reduced to a minimum, and since they were near to the cylinder ends the volume of the waste space was less, whilst the working steam and exhaust passed through separate channels, thus avoiding the loss of heat which was inevitable when a single port was used for both. Corliss, like Watt, realized that the valves should open and close rapidly for the best results, and releasing motions freeing the valve to allow it to close under the action of a spring dashpot system were as much the Corliss principle as was the use of separate valves for inlet and exhaust steam. The circular valves were left free to adjust themselves within the operating mechanism, and so were self-tightening, and with the use of very hard metal these remained steam-tight for many years on end. Watt's disengaging gear for the valves used weights to close them upon release, but Corliss used springs and dashpots to close the inlet valves to cut off the steam. At first Corliss used small flat sliding valves, but he soon developed the circular type which were fitted to thousands of cylinders from the mid-nineteenth century for as long as large steam engines were built.

Equilibrium Drop Valve (Hornblower, 1800) The use of flat swinging valves for the earliest engines has been noted above, but the single disc or 'beat' valve with its pressure only on one side required much effort to operate. The single disc valve of Watt served as long as it was small and the steam pressure was low, but as engine sizes and steam pressures increased the effort to open them against the load caused many difficulties, and in 1800 Hornblower made the significant development of this type by using two discs upon the same spindle (Fig. 21). By this means the downward load upon one valve disc equalled the upward load upon the other one, creating the 'equilibrium' valve. As in this the loading upon the valve gear was only the weight of the valve, it was virtually without friction and operated easily with the highest temperatures and pressures. This type of valve was used for all sizes of Cornish engines, for mill beam engines, and also for colliery engines up to the largest sizes when the valves were up to 18 inches in diameter. Although more noisy than sliding valves they were little trouble in operation, but for the very large continental engines built towards the end of the reciprocating steam-engine period of electrical generating stations, the stresses inherent from the weight and the need for high lifts to give ample port area in the very large cylinders led to the use of three and sometimes four seats above each other on one valve. Such valves were very complex and difficult to keep steam-tight, so they were not widely used.

Drop-piston Valve (from 1900) The last major development in valve design, drop-piston valves consisted of an arrangement of four short piston valves for each cylinder, with one at each end to control the steam inlet, and another at each end for the exhaust. They were simple bobbins fitted with spring rings on the outside which worked in ported liners. They worked with little friction and, since there were no seats, they were very quiet, coming to rest whilst covering the port into the cylinder. They were also light in weight and could operate at high speeds. They were used on the Continent, and as patented by Morley in England they gave very good service with superheated steam.

Thus the main types of valve needed to control the steam events in the cylinder were tried and established very early, but each – the semi-rotating (the cock), the sliding (flat and piston valves) and the dropping disc – underwent many changes in the two centuries of steam-engine construction and use.

Valve Gears A simple mechanism served to operate the valves of a steam engine, usually consisting of an eccentric mounted upon the crankshaft, although cams were sometimes used. Fig. 22 illustrates this arrangement for a slide valve. The sheave 'A' is a disc, usually made in halves for convenience in fitting it upon the crankshaft, with its centre offset to that of the shaft. The motion produced was small, and was transmitted to the valve by a strap and rod ('B'). To secure the correct relationship of the valve and piston movements, the eccentric centre was set at an angle of 90 degrees ahead of the crank, and to allow the steam to be expanded during the stroke it was necessary to add 'lap' ('L') to the valve, which in turn necessitated the eccentric being set even further ahead of the crank (i.e. angular advance 'AV'). There were of course many variations to this simple type evolved over the years. The engine could readily be made to run in either direction by fitting two eccentrics, one for the forward and one for the reverse motion, and connecting the ends of the eccentric rods by a link which could be moved across the valve rod to connect with either. Expansion and steam cut-off could be varied by placing the link in intermediate positions.

The provision of separate inlet and exhaust valves for each end of the cylinder eliminated some of the failings of the slide valve, as each operation was independent of the others and required a separate drive. Fig. 23 indicates one method of doing this, in which the eccentric oscillates a wrist plate 'A' on a pin on the side of the cylinder, with four pins in the wrist plate to operate the valves. Complete independence of the steam events was gained by connecting the inlet valves through a releasing mechanism which allowed each valve to close independently of the wrist plate motion.

Such valve gears were suited to general-purpose engines with rotating shafts, but not to single-acting engines working upon the Cornish cycle, in which the duty performed was governed by the number of strokes made per minute. This required that each cycle should be independent of the others, which was provided for by making a pause between the beginning of each cycle by holding the steam and exhaust valves closed until they were permitted to open by a mechanism called the 'cataract' (Fig. 24). In this the valves were operated by arbors or cross-shafts ('AR'), on the ends of which were fitted sectors ('SC'), which were locked by the catches 'B', whose position was determined by stops in the loop 'C', which was under the control of the cataract ('CT'). This comprised a plunger pump ('P') immersed in a tank of water, the pump being raised by the wiper arm 'WA' from a buffer 'BF' on the plug rod 'PR' operated from the engine beam. As the beam made the down stroke the arm 'WA' raised the plunger and filled the space below with water through the valve 'IV', the water being only able to escape through the hand-controlled valve 'RV'. As long as the catches held the sectors the engine could not begin another cycle, but as the water escaped from below the plunger by the cock, the plunger sank, raising the releasing rod 'RR' until the pin in 'C' lifted 'B', so freeing the sector 'SC' and allowing the weight on the arbor to rotate it to open first the exhaust and then the steam valves for another cycle. In this manner a large engine, often with a total of hundreds of tons of moving parts, was controlled by a small hand-operated valve.

STEAM BOILERS AND EXHAUST STEAM

Steam Boilers The evolution of the boiler largely parallels that of the steam engine. The history of the steam engine may be seen as a battle for ever higher efficiency, and the efficiency of a steam engine was largely governed by the difference in the temperature of entry and rejection of the working fluid – steam. To maximize this differential it is necessary to increase the initial temperature and pressure of the steam, and this calls for improvements in the techniques of boiler construction. As a broad principle, boilers divide into two main service requirements – the stationary and the movable. The latter is subject to more severe restrictions of weight and space than the former, and as a result movable boilers were usually cased in metal with a minimum of brickwork while the stationary boilers normally had a brick-built case. In both forms the steam boiler developed enormously over two hundred years.

The Haystack Boiler (Newcomen, from 1712) The success of the Savery engine, requiring steam of some pressure, had been severely limited by the inability of craftsmen at the end of the seventeenth century to provide suitable boilers. The Newcomen engine, on the other hand, simply required a large volume of condensable vapour at atmospheric pressure, and a few of the earliest boilers in Cornwall were made of stone with copper internal flues. The normal boiler used with the Newcomen engine, however, was the 'haystack', so called from its resemblance in shape to this farmyard feature. This could be made by a blacksmith from the small wrought-iron plates which were all that the forges of the time could produce. Usually circular in plan, it was frequently made of great size, sometimes as much as 20 feet in diameter, for as a rule only the largest engines were provided with more than one boiler. The great volume of water contained was an asset, since the engine drew a large amount of steam at each stroke. This type of boiler was very wasteful if used only occasionally, but when, as at many collieries, it was almost constantly kept at work, the hot-brick setting of the boiler proved economical and it required only unskilled attention. It was customary to dome the bottom of the boiler upwards slightly and to carry the gases from the fire around the boiler shell, and for all its failings it gave very good service, serving Newcomen engines for some 150 years (see Fig. 9). A few hay-stack boilers survive today, including one at Blist's Hill Open Air Museum, Ironbridge.

The Wagon Boiler (Watt, from 1780) James Watt's improvements in the steam engine, making it a tool for everyday use in factories and mills, demanded a very different boiler structure. Not only was steam required at pressure, albeit as low as 5–7 psi, but also the boiler had to be more adaptable to raising and stopping steam production daily, and with increasing use of the steam engine in towns, where fuel was expensive, evaporative efficiency became a serious matter. To meet these new needs Watt invented his 'wagon' boiler (see Figs. 10 and 11). This consisted of a rectangular water chamber set in brickwork, long and narrow and with a domed top, and with the sides and bottom of the shell curved inwards to increase its strength. It was made in a specific series of sizes, and the larger boilers were fitted with an internal flue which increased the economy. As with the haystack boiler, the fire was below, with the gases passing all around the boiler sides on the way to the chimney, but where there was an internal flue the gases usually passed under the shell to the back and returned to the front through the inner flue, finally passing around the sides. This type of boiler was usually fitted with a gravity feed water supply system, with an inlet valve controlled by a float, and many were fitted with an automatic damper which closed as the steam pressure rose. There were also safety blow-off pipes which relieved the pressure when it became too high.

Like the haystack boiler it was readily accessible for internal cleaning, whilst the flues could be swept easily.

The Cornish Boiler (Trevithick, from 1803) The growing need for higher power and economy, and the knowledge that both were gained by raising the steam pressure, led to continuous efforts to increase the working pressure. Watt's wagon boiler, even when heavily stayed, could only partially meet this need, and the first successful step was Trevithick's circular boiler with an internal furnace introduced in 1803. This proved that safe boilers could be made for high pressures, as Arthur Woolf did also with boilers consisting of many small tubular sections. Trevithick's type became widely used, but the large internal flue of the Cornish boiler was weak when made in larger sizes as the demand for higher powers continued (see Fig. 13).

The Lancashire Boiler (Fairbairn, 1844) Boilers with two smaller internal flues than the one normally used in the Cornish boiler had been made long before the solution reached by Fairbairn and Hetherington in their patent of 1844 for the twin internal furnace boiler, but from then onwards the 'Lancashire' twin internal furnace type really set the scene for rapid developments. Many plain circular boilers without flues had been made since 1830, and continued to be made and widely used throughout the nineteenth century in places where fuel was cheap, but it was the Lancashire boiler as manufactured by Galloways and others which provided the steam for the growth in engine power and the size of mills in the second half of the century (see Fig. 14).

Tubular Boilers (from 1829) The locomotive, needing high power with small space and weight, and the steamship, with similar requirements, promoted the extensive use of tubular heating surfaces, and with such free-steaming designs progress was rapid, so that by 1870 locomotives were powerful when using steam up to 120 psi, whilst the ability of marine boilers to give high power for the weight and space alone led to the great powers of naval vessels at that time, developing up to 9,000 hp with steam of only 30 psi. The development of the compound engine at sea called for higher pressures, as coal consumption was reduced from $4\frac{1}{2}$ lb per hour in the simple expansion marine engines of 1865 to $1\frac{3}{4}$ lb in the best triple expansion engines of 1885. Such pressures were obtained from boilers which were almost entirely of circular section, although on land the loco-motive boiler retained the flat-sided firebox until the end.

Water-tube Boilers (from the 1860s) There was experiment with other types of boiler throughout the nineteenth century, and the steam carriages of the 1820s and 1830s were fitted with many designs of small water capacity, but little progress was made until the 1880s with boilers having the water inside the tubes. The first successful design was the Babcock & Wilcox which evolved from the 1860s so that, when the new electricity industry needed a high-capacity responsive boiler by the 1890s, it was able to meet the demand. Many similar types were developed for land service, and the growing need for safe, light boilers for torpedo boats and other small, fast naval vessels led to many three-drum designs.

Modern Boilers Development has proceeded along these lines, with increasing fuel costs requiring that boilers should be more responsive, and so virtually able to be turned on and off as steam is needed. The great steps forward in efficient automatic controls have greatly reinforced this development, as have the special needs of road transport, where the emergence of steam cars (1890–1910) required steam plant that would largely run itself, and at the same time meet the ever-varying power needs of the roads. Considerable success was secured in providing steam-ing capacity virtually off the shelf in such generators, and over the years the growing electricity industry, faced with equally variable needs, has met the problem in the same manner, with limited capacity in the boiler but high flexibility in the firing and water-feeding systems. Modern requirements are met in a similar fashion for the small steam user, with both shell and water-tube boilers being now built as packages, factory-assembled with their controls and connections upon a readily manœuvred base, which can be easily moved into position and set to work with a minimum of installation work on the site. For the large power stations, boilers of great capacity have now become vir-tually tubular boxes with immensely high fire-box heat output, and a similar development has occurred with marine boilers.

Exhaust Steam After passing through the engine, the used steam is exhausted or rejected from the cycle, and either condensed back to water – the usual practice in mill engines, power stations, and at sea – or else discharged into the funnel – as in the case of locomotive, traction, and portable engines, where it was used to increase the draught – or directly into the air as at collieries or small factories. Exhausting into the atmosphere (Fig. 13) was simpler and appropriate where water was chemically unsuitable for boiler feed from a jet condenser, or where the engine was too small to justify the cost of condensing the exhaust. This method of working, however, did involve the loss of all the feed-water and of a great deal of the heat remaining in the exhaust steam, although up to 10 per cent of this could be returned to the cycle by using the exhaust steam to heat the feed-water before it entered the boiler. Also, in industries where there was use for heat at moderate temperature (up to 220° F), much of the heat remaining in the exhaust could be recovered, and latterly it could be used in an exhaust steam turbine which could develop considerable power.

Condensing was achieved either by spraying cold water into the steam (the jet condenser), in which case the steam and the water mixed (see Figs. 9, 10, 11 and 14), or else by contact with cooled surfaces (the surface condenser), in which case the steam and the water did not mix (see Fig. 17). The condenser was an enclosed chamber at the end of the exhaust pipe, and condensing the steam created a vacuum which added greatly to the power of the engine. However, since there was always some air in the steam, and the condensed water collected in the condenser, a separate pump (the air-pump) was provided to remove both and thus to maintain the vacuum.

The air-pump was usually a simple bucket pump in which the air and water moved in one direction only, and it could be driven from any convenient part of the engine motion, but for the very high vacuum needed for the large power-station turbines, steam jets are used as air-pumps, starting with Sir Charles Parsons' vacuum augmenter of 1902. Today centrifugal pumps are used to remove the water, and jets for the air.

CHAPTER SIX

The Engine-Builders

As the mechanization of industry spread in Britain to even the smallest concerns in comparatively isolated places, it created a widespread demand for the skills of engine-building and engine-maintenance, so that enterprising men who were able and willing to practise these skills established firms in all parts of the country to meet the need. The people who entered the trade of engine-builder had frequently acquired their skills as millwrights and in similar crafts which required long and arduous apprenticeships. They acquired capital from their savings, or by borrowing from relatives and friends, or by entering into partnership with men of business who saw some profit in supplying industry with the new machines which it needed. Together, such people laid the foundations of the modern engineering industry in the eighteenth and early nineteenth century: the famous partnership between the craftsman and inventor James Watt and the shrewd businessman Matthew Boulton was outstanding, but it was not untypical, and it was from the success of enterprises such as *Boulton & Watt* that the British lead in industrial mechanization and steam technology was largely derived. Almost all the great firms of steam-engine makers have now disappeared from the trade directories, the victims of changing techniques or commercial take-overs. Most of them never grew beyond small companies employing a few dozen men, able to undertake a wide range of engineering maintenance jobs, and to build the occasional steam engine. Many of them, however, may be recalled to notice by their names cast upon the beds of the engines which they made, and by the distinctive features which they gave to their engines. For this reason alone it is worth reviewing the contribution of the engine-builders to the evolution of the steam engine.

It should be emphasized at the outset that many of the engine-builders with whom we are concerned were small firms and that their business was usually extremely varied. Even though more is known about the few large companies which produced most of the engines, much of the routine work of fitting, maintenance, and repair was performed by small-scale operators who are almost entirely forgotten, but who none the less played a very significant part in local developments of the engineering industry. They often functioned with the minimum of equipment even though they had to carry an extensive stock of spare parts and fittings. A good example of this type of enterprise was *Carters* of Salford, who had fine craftsmen capable of making parts and tools of every type, even to thread-cutting equipment of the most outrageous specifications, in 48 hours. The works was destroyed in the air raids of 1940–41. As such firms developed, they frequently started their own foundries, increasing their capabilities, and assuming the proud title of 'Ironworks', like the *Burnley Ironworks*, specializing in millwork as well as engines, and the *Reading Ironworks*, which made a wide range of agricultural machinery. The term was also applied to such large engine-building firms as *Musgraves* of Bolton and others which often, when busy, employed up to 800 men.

Substance was given to the modern conception of the engineer very largely by these early nineteenth-century pioneers, to whom the building of a bridge, a boiler, a boat, or a beam engine, were all items to be taken in their stride. The craft of engine-building was thus integral to the day-to-day maintenance of industry, with local engineering works, which could not have survived by specializing in one sector alone, providing a good living for many employees by building engines, repairing machinery, or altering factory layouts, and at the same time training first-class mechanics as apprentices. Certainly the trade was very versatile, but it did nevertheless tend to concentrate specialized branches in particular areas. An excellent example of this regional specialization can be seen in the Eastern Counties, where, starting in a small way of business, concerns such as *Marshalls* of Gainsborough, *Robeys* of Lincoln, and *Garretts* of Leiston, to name but a few, developed to become household names wherever agriculture evolved beyond the primitive hand craft.

It is unfortunate that as far as general building is concerned there is very little record left that would indicate the scale of operations. But it can be established that *John Musgrave & Sons* of Bolton did complete 25 engines in 1906, 23 in 1895, and 15 in 1885,[1] whilst *Yates & Thom* over the period 1910–14 made several of the largest engines that they ever built, including three very powerful steam winding engines which gave some sixty years' service. It is notable that several firms built their largest engines almost at the end of their career.

MARINE ENGINES

During the nineteenth century marine-engine building tended to follow the iron shipbuilding industry in becoming concentrated in four major areas of northern Britain: on the estuaries of the Clyde, the Tyne, the Tees, and the Mersey. However, although these were the centres of the heaviest and greatest output, there were many other concerns spread more widely, most of them quite small firms. There were, too, a few engine- and boat-builders in unexpected places, such as *Edwin Clark* at Brimscombe near Stroud (later carried on by *Abdela Mitchell*), *Edward Hayes* at Stony Stratford, and *Yarwood* and *Pimblotts* at Northwich in Cheshire, who built engines as well as hulls for the Scottish West Coast 'puffers', some of which survived long and hard careers. Naval construction programmes had a powerful influence on marine-engine building and helped to maintain the traditional Thames-side engine-building industry at a time when shipbuilding was migrating towards the northern estuaries. The three major enterprises of *Maudslay Sons & Field*, *Penns*, and *Humphreys, Tennant & Co* were kept going largely by the substantial orders they received in the second half of the nineteenth century for engines for naval vessels, and they played a large part in the evolution of the naval marine engine. The last named of the three, *Humphreys, Tennant & Co*, was formed in 1850 when the young Charles Tennant (later Sir Charles, and grandson of the founder of the giant bleaching-powder firm at St Rollox in Glasgow) entered into partnership with Edward Humphreys, who was Chief Engineer at the Woolwich Dockyard. They completed their first contract at their Deptford marine engine works in 1854, and between then and 1907, when the works closed, the firm engined a dozen of the most important British warships of the period (including *Dreadnought* in 1875 and *Invincible* in 1907).[2]

In 1900, 36 per cent of all the marine steam engines built in Britain were constructed on Clyde-side. This amounted to a total of 457,136 hp built at 33 different firms in the business there, of which 12 specialized in engines only and had no shipyards.

This total represented 80 per cent of the marine engines built in Scotland, but even that vast output was influenced by naval work as the fall in the number of engines supplied to the Royal Navy in 1900 caused a reduction in the total horse power from that achieved in 1898 and 1899. Of the firms building only engines, seven built a total of 105 engines in 1900, with *David Rowan* (15 sets developing 27,000 hp) and *Dunsmuir & Jackson* (15 sets developing 28,800 hp) in the lead, and *Muir & Houston* (23 sets, mainly for trawlers and other small vessels, developing a little under 15,000 hp) also figuring prominently. A number of Clyde-side engines were sent abroad, as with *McKie & Baxter* who exported 14 of their 20 engines.[3]

In 1907 there was a total of 104 firms building marine engines in the United Kingdom, producing a total of 1,781,000 hp, but by this time the steam turbine has to be included in the figure. The *Lusitania* and *Mauretania* were each fitted with turbines generating 70,000 hp in 1907, and the reciprocating steam-engine power was probably about 1,500,000 hp in that year. Engines continued to be built by firms away from the main centres: *Hayes* at Stony Stratford built 425 hp, *Sissons* at Gloucester built 250 hp, *Elliott & Garrood* at Beccles built no less than 3,850 hp consisting largely of their special triple expansion design for trawlers, and *Mumfords* at Colchester and *Plentys* at Newbury each built nearly 6,000 hp, mainly for coasters and tugs. These figures indicate the continued vitality of the marine steam-engine business, even at a time when oil engines were coming into use for marine services.[4]

WINDING ENGINES

Winding engines for raising minerals in the mining industry were usually made by a small number of firms who also manufactured other mining machinery. They were widely spread, and only a few of the leading companies can be mentioned. *John Wood & Co.*, *Walkers*, and the *Worsley Mesnes Co.* were all in Wigan; *Daglish's* at St Helens; *J. & D. Leigh* at Patricroft; *Thornewill & Warham* at Burton-on-Trent; *Bradley & Craven* at Wakefield (where they also made brickmaking machinery); *Charles Markham & Co.* at Chesterfield; whilst *Robeys* at Lincoln made excellent fast engines which were sent all over the world. *John Fowler* made winding engines in Leeds, and those made by *Fraser & Chalmers* at Erith in Kent were as universally celebrated as those made by their American associates. In Scotland, *Fullerton, Hodgart & Barclay* of Paisley, and *Andrew Barclay* of Kilmarnock, are justly celebrated wherever minerals are raised, and *Douglas & Grant* of Kirkcaldy are also well known for their winding engines as well as for rice-preparation machinery and many mill engines. Between them these firms also supplied most of the ancillary machinery for the mining industry, although fans were also supplied by *Waddells* of Llanelly, amongst numerous others. A handful of Cornish firms supplied the many winders ('whims' as they were called in Cornwall) needed for the great number of shafts used over many years in the tin and copper mines of that county. The three leading concerns were *Harvey & Co.* of Hayle, the *Copperhouse Foundry* also of Hayle, and the *Perran Foundry*, who between them made the huge Dutch drainage engines and the largest beam blowing engines ever built. Pumping water was a vast engine operation, for mining as well as waterworks, and Cornish engine-builders provided the engines, boilers, and pitwork for pumps in the county which went down as far as 3,000 feet. Cornwall has the distinction of having made the three largest steam engines ever built, which were those for the Dutch drainage scheme of Lake Haarlem in the 1840s, of which one, the Cruquius engine, survives. This was built by *Harvey & Co.* and was completed in 1849. The casting, transport, and erection of these engines was an enormous task, indicating the resourcefulness of the Cornish engine-builders.

WATERWORKS ENGINES

Waterworks engineers were also in the lead in the search for increased engine efficiency, and two firms were outstanding: *Hathorn Davey & Co.* of Leeds, and *Worthington Simpson* of London (and later Newark-on-Trent). *Hathorn Davey* followed *Carrett Marshalls* at the Sun Foundry in Leeds in 1872, and from the start Henry Davey was the leading personality. He favoured the direct-acting compound design, usually horizontal for deep-mine shaft pumps, with the application of the differential system, by which the leverage between the piston and the pump rods was varied, allowing high expansion of the steam against the constant pump loading. Direct-acting engines had no crank and flywheel to control the extent of the piston motion. Davey also introduced the differential valve control system, by which the damage was prevented when the engine moved too rapidly in the event of a pump or pipe failure. This type was made into the present century. Few now remain, but that at Cheddars Lane Pumping Station, Cambridge, is a good example (see Plate 9).

James Simpson & Co. of Pimlico were early leaders in the field of economical pumping engines, adopting compounding in rotative beam engines in the mid-nineteenth century. In 1886 the firm secured a licence to build the *Worthington* direct-acting engine which, with the compensating system, gave high economy with a small compact engine and no rotative action. The venture was highly successful, as by 1908 they had made over 510 of these engines, including 20 for the Coolgardie water scheme in Australia. This involved eight pumping stations to pump 5,600,000 gallons per day through a 330-mile pipeline. *Worthington Simpson* were the only firm able to meet the stringent conditions laid down for this very large contract.

From these special designs both firms developed engines for the highest fuel economy, and there was considerable rivalry between them until reciprocating engines were superseded by steam turbines and the electrically driven turbo-pump, which have now become standard pumping equipment in waterworks. Both firms, incidentally, manufacture large numbers of these new pumping machines. Many other firms did much to aid the supply of pure water and the improvement of land drainage in the second half of the nineteenth century, including *Easton & Anderson* of Erith (Kent) and *Gwynnes* of Hammersmith, who developed the centrifugal pump for low lifts. *Ashton & Frost* of Blackburn also made fine economical waterworks engines. *W. H. Allen* of Bedford made the largest steam-turbine-powered pumping plant ever designed in Europe with their contract of 1938 for the Metropolitan Water Board works at Hampton, comprising eight steam turbines of some 12,000 hp, driving turbine pumps and electrical generators for other pumps.

ENGINES FOR THE METAL TRADES

The growth of the British iron and steel industry was greatly assisted by the ability of engine-builders to deliver promptly engines capable of developing the very high power and other special features required for the rapid working of hot metal for rails, sheets, and the tinplate trades. Foremost among the engine-builders who met these needs in the nineteenth century and later were such firms as *Galloways* of Manchester, *Lambertons* of Coatbridge, *Charles Markham* of Chesterfield, and *Davy Bros.* of Sheffield.

HIGH-SPEED ENGINES
In the last phase of the evolution of the reciprocating steam engine, the advantages of enclosed forced-lubrication engines led many firms of engine-builders to enter this field. Besides *Belliss & Morcom* of Birmingham, the leading names were *W. H. Allen* of Bedford, *Browett & Lindley* of Patricroft and later Letchworth, *Dodmans* of King's Lynn, *Robeys* of Lincoln, *Readers* of Nottingham, *Ashworth & Parker* of Bury, *McLarens* of Leeds, *Easton & Bessemer* of Taunton, *Sissons* of Gloucester, *Maclellan* of Glasgow, *Fullerton Hodgarts* of Paisley, and *Howdens* of Glasgow. The enclosed engine became the most widely used steam engine type, and from about 1935 they were, together with small marine engines, almost the only designs of reciprocating steam engine made in Britain. Even in these services, however, other sources of power have now largely superseded the piston engine.

TEXTILE-MILL ENGINES
The most spectacular engines, ones which could be seen from many streets in Lancashire, Yorkshire, and Cheshire, were those driving the textile mills. They were not the most powerful, nor by any means the largest, but they were probably the most numerous of the higher-power steam engines, and both visually and economically they represented the steam engine at its best. Rather fuller information is available upon the builders of the mill engines than on most of the others, and so it is possible to give a summary of the best-known firms in Britain. It was a tribute to their versatility as designers and constructors that they were able to build engines for other services than those of the textile mills, and frequently engines requiring very different characteristics in operation.

Providing power for the textile mills was big business in the nineteenth century, and in its heyday there were at least thirty firms in Britain employing over 20,000 men in this business with the resources to make large engines. All the leading firms did millwork and repairs, and alterations to increase power and economy, but all had the facilities for large casting or forging, and the larger establishments frequently did this as outwork for the smaller ones. It was often the sheer size and costs of such works which led to failures when, as in the 1920s, the volume of work fell off, except for the few which survived by diversifying their business.

Daniel Adamson & Co. of Newton Moor Ironworks, Dukin-field: Established in 1851, this firm made mill, pumping, colliery, rolling-mill, and air-compressing engines, some with slide valves, but mostly with Wheelock valves fitted under a licence taken out in 1886, and some with drop-piston valves after 1900. They made the 'Lancashire Witch' portable engines in the 1860s, the first triple expansion mill engine in 1863, and the first quadruple expansion mill engine in 1870.

Ashton Frost & Co. of Bank Top Foundry, Blackburn: This firm was established by four partners as a foundry in 1870 and began engine-building in the early 1880s, mainly making engines for weaving sheds, and later large pumping engines also. They usually fitted slide or Corliss valves, but made at least one drop-valve engine for a weaving shed. Their last engines were probably those made for Allenby Shed and for Shanghai Waterworks in the 1920s, the firm closing down in 1926.

Buckley & Taylor of Castle Ironworks, Oldham: The output of this firm, established in 1861, was almost entirely beam, horizontal, and vertical mill engines, with Corliss or slide valves, and mill gearing. They fitted at least four types of Corliss trip gear and made many economical slide-valve engines in the 1880s, and the last beam engines for a cotton mill. From 1900 they manufactured mainly vertical engines. Their last and largest engine, installed in 1926, was that at Wye No. 2 Mill, a horizontal cross compound of 2,500 hp, but they remain in business as general engineers.

Burnley Ironworks of Burnley: Beginning as *Marslands* in the 1830s, they made large beam engines from the 1840s. They were owned by William Bracewell in the 1860s and were re-formed as Burnley Ironworks on his death in 1887, with a capital of £20,000. The firm manufactured mostly horizontal cross compound and tandem weaving-shed engines, but only three verticals, all with slide or Corliss valves. They closed in 1927.

James Carmichael & Co. of Ward Foundry, Dundee: Founded in 1810, this firm manufactured engines of all types with slide, Corliss, or drop-piston valves, and uniflows, for mills, colliery winding, blast-furnace blowing, and marine service. They also

E

made water turbines, hydraulic plant, boilers and plate work, and did forging and casting as outwork for other firms. They made mill engines up to 2,500 hp with flywheels up to 120 tons, and latterly the Carmac steam turbine. Closed 1927.

Clayton & Goodfellow of Atlas Works, Blackburn: Later general engineers, they were established in 1857 and built beam, horizontal, tandem and cross compound, vertical and uniflow engines, with slide, Corliss, or drop valves. Most of their engines were below 700 hp, but they also made some large colliery winding engines. Their Corliss trip gear was very efficient and trouble-free. They probably made their last engine in the mid-1920s.

Cole Marchent & Morley, of Prospect Foundry, Bradford, Yorks: Established in 1848, this firm made engines for mills, colliery winding, pumping, air-compressing, etc. They early used drop valves and then slide and Corliss valves. They were best known for their highly efficient drop-piston valves in later years, and also for uniflow engines, and they made some gas engines and producers.

Douglas & Grant Ltd of Dunnikier Foundry, Kirkcaldy, Fife: Founded at Cupar in 1846, they moved to Kirkcaldy in the 1850s. They made beam, horizontal, and vertical engines for mills, pumping, and colliery-winding services, and, from 1860, rice-milling equipment and engines of the largest size. They early developed Corliss valves, having fitted 16 engines with them by 1867. They made drop valves by 1905 and uniflows after 1912.

Fullerton Hodgart & Barclay of Vulcan Foundry, Paisley: They were established in 1838 and made mill, winding, air-compressing, and pumping engines, with slide, piston, Corliss, or drop valves, to the largest sizes, and also did general engineering work. They made at least one reversing rolling-mill engine, hydraulic presses and cranes of all types, and, more recently, electric winders, which now enjoy a world-wide reputation. They also made marine engines for the Royal Navy in both World Wars.

W. & J. Galloway Ltd of Knott Mill, Manchester: The original partners started as millwrights in 1790 and were joined by another Scot in 1820. In 1835 they started at Knott Mill as engine-builders, and were involved in locomotive manufacture in its early years. They made mill engines as well as pumping and rolling-mill engines of the largest sizes, with slide, piston, Corliss, and drop valves. They also made uniflow and steam-extraction and high-power gas engines, and at least one colliery winding engine. From 1845 they developed a large boiler business, later making one 'Lancashire' boiler a day for many years. Their last engine was a uniflow for a South Wales sheet mill in 1929, and their last boiler was made in 1931 before they closed in 1932.

Benjamin Goodfellows of Hyde: Founded in 1838, this firm made mostly large mill engines, with flywheels up to 32 feet diameter, and also refrigerating and air-compressing machinery. They made and altered many beam engines, and took up Corliss valves early, having made 80 such cylinders by 1880. Many of their engines had heavy gear drives, but their largest engine was for rope drive at Astley Mill. The works were sold in 1903 and their successors built small engines.

Hick Hargreaves & Co. of Soho Ironworks, Bolton: This firm was established in 1832 and made a wide range of steam power plant for mills, rolling mills, furnace blowing, and heat extraction, as well as turbines. They were amongst the first to take up Corliss valves and later made drop-valve and uniflow engines, diesel engines, and many boilers. The firm maintained a very substantial output up to the largest sizes for many years, their last engine being a uniflow exported to Turkey in 1935. In later years they developed an extensive business in high-vacuum condensers. The firm is still in existence, although no longer engaged in the manufacture of textile-mill engines.

Marsdens Engines Ltd of Heckmondwike, Yorks: The output of this firm, established in 1870, was mainly horizontal and vertical mill engines, with slide or Corliss valves and a few uniflows. They undertook extensive engine repairing in later years, and closed about 1960.

J. & W. McNaught Ltd of St George's Foundry, Rochdale: McNaughts were established in 1860 and moved to St George's in 1862. From making small engines they moved on to building large ones in 1874, as a partnership with the above style. They were the main rivals to *Petries*, and like that firm they mainly used twist piston valves and Corliss valves, but fitted at least one set of drop-valve cylinders in 1912. They made 95 engines in 40 years, developing a total of 80,000 hp, before closing down in 1914.

John Musgrave & Sons of Globe Ironworks, Bolton: Established in 1832, this firm made beam, horizontal, and vertical engines, with slide, Corliss, and drop valves, for mills, colliery winding, rolling mills, air-compressing, and electricity generating. They were the first to build Stumpf uniflow engines in Britain in

1910. The firm had a large boiler business and built a new boiler shop at Westhoughton in 1902. A branch of the family started cotton spinning in 1862 and remained in the business for over a century, always with Musgrave engines. The engine-building firm closed in 1931, when they had made over 1,460 engines.

Newton Bean & Mitchell of Dudley Hill, Bradford: This firm, established in 1896, concentrated mainly on modern types of mill engines with Corliss and drop-piston valves. They undertook much engine repairing in later years, and made their last engine about 1936.

John Petrie & Sons of Whitehall Street, Rochdale: Beginning as millwrights in Bury in 1793, the firm established Whitehall Street Foundry in 1814 and made their first steam engine in 1819. Their output was largely beam, horizontal, and a few vertical mill engines, with slide, piston, and Corliss valves, and latterly with Swiss-designed drop valves. They largely used Dowell trip motion for Corliss valves. The firm closed in 1912, having made a total of about 185 engines in 90 years of engine-building. Until 1883 all their engines were under 1,000 hp, but after that date they went up to 2,000 hp.

Pollit & Wigzell of Bank Foundry, Sowerby Bridge, Yorks: Founded by Timothy Bates in 1786, the firm were largely millwrights until 1834, when John Pollit started engine-building. He was joined by E. Wigzell in 1865, and they probably made as many mill engines as any other firm. Mainly beams to 1870, their later engines were mostly horizontal tandem and cross compound, with slide, Corliss, and drop-piston valves, up to 2,000 hp, and they made one uniflow. The firm also built some marine engines. The last steam engine was built in 1923 and the firm closed in 1931.

William Roberts & Co. of Phoenix Foundry, Nelson, Lancs: The output of this firm, founded in the mid-nineteenth century, was mainly horizontal tandem and cross compound engines, with slide and (after 1896) Corliss valves, and also a few inverted vertical engines. They dealt mainly with weaving sheds, and always did much mill gearing, and made the last geared flywheel for Bishop House Mill after a smash in 1950. Closed about 1960.

Thomas Robinson of Rochdale: Best known for woodworking machinery, this firm also made a total of some 900 engines between 1863 and 1913. Most of them were small engines, the largest being of 500 hp, but they amounted to a total of 20,000 hp.

George Saxon of Openshaw, Manchester: Established in 1854, Saxons concentrated almost entirely on mill engines, usually of horizontal tandem, cross compound, and inverted vertical designs, with slide, Corliss, and drop valves. They also built some Manhattans, but not beam, winding, pumping, or uniflow engines. They supplied numerous new cylinders for engines of other makes. Their last engine, in 1926, was a horizontal cross compound Corliss.

Scott & Hodgson of Guide Bridge Ironworks, near Manchester: The firm was founded in 1854 and bought by Edward Scott on the death of the first proprietor. With his partner, Henry Hodgson, Scott began engine-building in 1882, making mostly mill engines with slide, piston, Corliss, and drop valves. The firm also made inverted vertical and triple expansion engines of large sizes, often with piston valves for the low-pressure cylinders. They specialized in schemes where one large engine was arranged to drive several sections of a mill, and made four very large rolling-mill engines for John Summers of Shotton as well as doing much work for South Wales sheet mills. Their last steam engines before closure in 1952 were sent to India in 1927.

S. S. Stott & Sons of Laneside Foundry, Haslingden: Established from Lindsays Foundry in 1866, they made beam and horizontal, and a few vertical, engines for mills, and beams for waterworks. They also made Benns patent condenser and air-pump, and latterly did much work for the gas industry. Their largest and last engine was built for Halsteads in 1926 and developed 1,000 hp.

Urmson & Thompson of Hathershaw Ironworks, Oldham: This firm was founded in the 1860s and specialized mainly in mill gearing, but they also built six or seven engines. Their largest engine was for the Ace Mill and their largest single contract was for the Nile Mill gearing in 1899. The firm closed down about 1926.

John & Edward Wood of Victoria Foundry, Bolton: The firm assumed this title in the 1860s when the Woods took over from *Knight & Wood*, as which it had been established in 1838. The Woods soon began making horizontal engines, and after 1870 placed all of the Corliss valves at the bottom of the cylinder, giving high economy. Their designer McBeth had several specialities to his credit, such as metallic packing and a patent engine design. The firm is said to have closed with uncompleted engines in the works in 1912.

Wood Brothers of Valley and Prospect Foundries, Sowerby Bridge, Yorks: Founded in 1850, this firm made beam, vertical, and horizontal mill engines, with slide, piston, Corliss, and at least one drop, valves. They also used piston valves with the Woods patent revolving motion for preventing the ridging of the ports. They supplied most of the engines for Joseph Rank's flour mills. Their largest textile-mill engines were for Shiloh Mills, Royton. The firm closed down about 1924.

Woodhouse & Mitchell of Clifton Bridge Works, Sowerby Bridge, Yorks: Established by four employees of other firms, Messrs Wood, Baldwin, Mitchell and Woodhouse, in 1867, this was made a public company in 1902. They constructed horizontal and vertical engines with slide and Corliss valves for flour mills all over the world, as well as for woollen and cotton mills in Britain, and two uniflow engines. They also made wire-drawing machinery, mill gearing, and cranes of many types. Spare engines were kept in the shops in case of emergencies, and they fitted several of these to keep mills running after breakdowns. Their last and probably largest engine was one of 1,000 hp for Owler Ings Mill in 1923, and they carried out a major overhaul of a large mill beam engine in Yorkshire in 1926. The firm closed down in 1966.

Yates & Thom Ltd of Canal Ironworks, Blackburn: Begun by William and John Yates as millwrights in 1826, they also built water wheels in the 1850s and in 1868 installed the large beam engines and mill gearing for the India Mill, Darwen. They made many slide-valve engines for the cotton trade, waterworks, etc., adopting Corliss valves in the 1880s and drop valves from 1900, and later they built some uniflow engines. They built very large mill, colliery, winding, and waterworks pumping engines, and a few for rolling mills. Although most of the works records were lost in a fire, it is certain that their output of engines in the first 14 years of the present century was very great, as there is evidence that they received orders for 14 engines in 1903, 9 in 1904, 23 in 1905, 23 in 1906, and 22 in 1907, while in 1911–13 they built three of the largest winding engines ever made for collieries, one in Lancashire and two similar ones for the then expanding Yorkshire coalfield around Doncaster. Their last steam engines were winders for South Africa in 1938. The firm closed down recently.

CHAPTER SEVEN

Conclusion:
The Steam Engine in Perspective

Although the reciprocating stationary steam engine has now passed out of normal use, it is worth assessing, by way of recapitulation and summary, the nature of its service to British industry and marine engineering. Moreover, as the engines have now been disappearing rapidly for two decades, it will be appropriate to conclude this survey of the industrial archaeology of the steam engine by considering the engines which still remain and the problems of preservation which they pose.

The extent of steam power in Britain defies precise quantification. For one thing, the available statistics are incomplete or not sufficiently discriminating: nineteenth-century statisticians were extremely interested in the output of manufactured commodities and in exports and imports, but their figures of steam power are frequently expressed in numbers of looms or spindles driven, or by total horse powers which do not distinguish between steam and other sources of power. Another reason for imprecision is that steam power became so all-pervasive that it was largely taken for granted. Even though it always co-existed with the industrial use of water power and came increasingly to compete with electricity and the internal combustion engine, it became from the time Watt perfected rotative motion up to the First World War the universal maid-of-all-work. Steam engines in all shapes and sizes were installed for every imaginable industrial purpose and for a great number of other purposes also: on the farm, in fair-grounds, and in all sorts of public services. The result was that they became virtually uncountable, particularly as they frequently remained in service for a very long time, so that at any one moment there were steam engines of a wide variety of vintages in operation. We have already observed that several Newcomen engines remained in use into the present century, even though in most technical respects they had long been rendered obsolete. Such persistence makes the assessment of total steam power at any one point in time a completely daunting exercise.

However, even though precision is unattainable, estimates have been made of the growth of steam power, and we have already made use of some of these. They tend to rely heavily on the records kept by well-organized firms such as Boulton & Watt, the achievement of which in producing a total of 496 engines in the 25 years when the Watt patent could be enforced by the company has been described. But this figure was certainly only a fraction of the total steam engines existing in the country. It has been estimated that at least 300 Newcomen engines had been built by 1775[1] and many more new ones were constructed after that. There were also a number of engines built on the Savery cycle in the eighteenth century. Several have been identified in Lancashire, where they were built by Joshua Wrigley and other engineers to raise water in order to operate a conventional water wheel.[2] After 1800 the situation quickly became even more complex, with manufacturers springing up all over the country to make, install and maintain steam engines, and our information about engines and their performance inevitably becomes highly selective as it depends largely upon the accidental survival of the records of a few manufacturers. Of these, reference has been made to several in this book, such as the Cornish engineers whose detailed records of their machines did much to increase thermal efficiency in the first half of the nineteenth century, and, at second hand, the facts on which commentators like Andrew Ure based their observations on the general condition of British industrial growth and on the crucial role of steam power in this process.

One fact which stands out from all these estimates is the overwhelming contribution of steam power to British prosperity. We have quoted the comments of mid-nineteenth-century observers to show how they were amazed and even somewhat bemused by the impact of steam on industrial production and the new railway system. By the end of the century this sense of wonder had been tempered by a certain anxiety: the steam engine no longer seemed to be a British monopoly, and other prime movers were beginning to challenge it. But reliance upon steam power remained immense, and it was only gradually in the twentieth century that it began to lose ground, although after 1918 the rate of decline became pronounced, accelerating rapidly in the middle decades of the century. It is notable that the steam engine remained strongest where it had first been strong – in the staple British industries of textiles, coal mining, metallic mining, and iron and steel – and that its fortunes were to a large extent identified with the decline of these industries. Thus the virtual extinction of the Cornish tin and copper industry left the landscape of Cornwall littered with some of the most spectacular industrial monuments in the country in the shape of hundreds of abandoned steam-engine houses; the decline of the Lancashire cotton industry deprived some of the finest mill engines in the world of their *raison d'être*; and, more recently, the rationalization of the coal industry has meant the elimination of many steam winding engines. Only the iron and steel industry retains its nineteenth-century pre-eminence, and here part of the cost of survival has been radical modernization of plant involving the transfer to electric rolling and the abandonment of steam power.

Meanwhile, in the new industries which have grown up in the present century, steam power has never been adopted on any scale. The giant automobile and electrical-engineering enterprises, for example, have always derived the bulk of their power from electricity, particularly as the spread of the National Grid has made this source generally available since the 1920s. Indeed, it is difficult to see how it could have been otherwise, for despite the high thermal efficiency of all the later steam engines, the task of raising steam called for additional boiler plant, maintenance, and labour, and required continuous working to achieve maximum economy of operation, so that steam ceased to be competitive with electricity in every industry where cost efficiency combined with high flexibility were important. In older establishments, such as some waterworks, where these factors have been less significant, steam power has survived, but in a dwindling role. New installations even in these services have usually derived their power from other sources, and the recent reorganization of the gas supply industry to accommodate natural gas has involved a further carnage of steam plant. The few stationary steam engines which remain operational are thus in old establishments such as some waterworks and breweries, or in some industries such as tobacco treatment, in which the exhaust steam has importance in the processing. Also, a few are maintained as stand-by units in hospitals and similar institutions, although even here the burden of keeping boilers up to standard is a difficulty making conversion to internal combustion attractive.

Nevertheless, it is a mistake to dismiss steam power as a thing of the past, for, as we have already argued, it remains, in the shape of the steam turbine, the most important source of power in advanced industrial societies today, providing electrical energy on a colossal and ever-increasing scale. What *is* a thing of the past is the reciprocating steam engine, for in spite of all the magnificent increases in efficiency indicated in the table below, the reciprocating engine has been made obsolete by electricity and other sources of energy. It is this very obsolescence which makes the stationary reciprocating steam engine so much a matter of concern to the industrial archaeologist.

Amount of coal necessary to develop one horse power per hour

1712	Newcomen engine	32 lb
1770	Newcomen as improved by Smeaton	17 lb
1790	Watt engine	9 lb
1830	Cornish engine	3 lb
1870	Compound marine engine	2 lb
1885	Triple expansion marine engine	$1\frac{1}{2}$ lb

(Source: Science Museum Catalogue of Stationary Engines, 1925, p. 32 *et seq.*)

Note: The last figure in this table represents a very high economy, but modern electricity-generating stations achieve significant improvement on this performance.

It is probably not far wide of the mark to estimate that there are about 600 reciprocating steam engines still in existence in Britain, but as many of these are either in very poor condition (sometimes preserved in pieces in museum stores, or rusting away in deserted engine houses) or in the possession of private individuals, we have merely listed a selection of these in our Gazetteer, describing only the engines which are most accessible or most worth attention. Others may turn up, however, as it is surprisingly easy to 'lose' a small or medium-sized steam engine in a workshop or in the cellar of a civic institution which does not want the disturbance or expense involved in calling in the demolition contractor to remove it. Thus it has become urgently necessary for industrial archaeologists to undertake a stock-taking exercise in order to devise priorities for preserving the best or most significant of the steam engines which are still capable of being saved from the breaker's hammer. We offer the following suggestions towards the framing of such a policy.

Of the Newcomen-type engine, very few survive, and the rarity alone of these machines should ensure the maximum protection for them. Apart from those preserved in the Science Museum, London, and other museums (including one in Dearborn, Michigan, saved by the exertions of Henry Ford), the only two known in Britain are the Hawksbury engine, re-erected at Dartmouth by the Newcomen Society in honour of Thomas Newcomen, and the Elsecar coal mine pumping engine, near Sheffield, which was scheduled as an ancient monument in 1972. The Boulton & Watt engines which survive from the seminal period of 1775–1800 are also sure of maximum care and protection, all those few which remain being in museums, including some excellent specimens in the Science Museum and one in the Royal Scottish Museum, Edinburgh. The firm later made the older of the engines at the Crofton Pumping Station on the Kennet and Avon Canal in Wiltshire: installed in 1812 and converted to the Cornish cycle in 1845, this is almost certainly the oldest steam engine in the world to be still taking steam. Its partner was installed in 1844, replacing one of the original pair.

It cannot be taken for granted that any engine dating after 1800 will be preserved, as is clearly indicated by the great wastage of Cornish engines in the twentieth century, even though many of them were of considerable age and distinction. Only a few Cornish engines survive, with a mere handful actually in Cornwall – one at the Levant mine; two at East Pool in Camborne (these three are now in the care of the National Trust, having been saved from destruction by the Cornish Engines Preservation Society, now the Trevithick Society); one in the company museum of Holman Brothers Ltd of Camborne; and the other being the Greensplat engine, which was moved to Wendron Forge in 1973 and re-erected there. It is salutary to contemplate the destruction of the vast number of these giants which were once at work in the metal mines, quarries, and clay-pits, as it indicates the vulnerability of these machines represented by the value of the scrap metal in them. Despite the loss of the engines, the preservation of a selection of their engine houses is a worth-while endeavour if these are not also to be allowed to disappear. Many of them are beautiful decorative features in the

Cornish landscape, and are highly susceptible to the encroach-
ments of 'development' and vandalism.

Outside Cornwall, a few typical Cornish engines survive in
widely scattered parts of the country such as Cromford, Derbyshire, and Prestongrange, near Edinburgh; but not, unfortunately, the unique set of six engines installed at Sudbrook in
Monmouthshire to pump water from the Severn Tunnel in
1886, which were cruelly scrapped in 1968. One of the two Bull
engines at the Sudbrook pumping station has, however, been
preserved by the Science Museum, and the other has gone to the
National Museum of Wales at Cardiff.

Even with the heavy losses of Cornish engines, it must be
reported that beam engines generally have been comparatively
well preserved, partly because they have an immediate visual
attraction which many later types lack, and partly because, being
the oldest arrangement of working steam engine, they have been
longer on the priority list of museums and preservationists than
later designs. The last beam in regular mill service was probably
that at Mirfield in Yorkshire, which was taken out of commission
in the mid-1960s. A beam engine is still at work in the Ram
Brewery, in London, and a few still perform water-pumping
duties, but for the most part they survive only as the result of
active preservation efforts. Most museums purporting to have
technological collections have at least one beam engine, and a
few have been preserved in their original engine houses. They
comprise a remarkable variety of shapes and sizes, ranging from
the small Easton & Amos engine from Pearsall's silk mill in
Taunton Museum to the colossal sewage-pumping engines
preserved in Crossness Pumping Station in South-East London
or the waterworks engines at Papplewick in Nottinghamshire.
They include many significant differences of design: Woolf
compounding is represented by the Blagdon pumping engines
at Blagdon, near Bristol, and McNaught compounding by engines
at Kelvingrove Museum, Glasgow, and at Bradford Museum of
Technology, although both are at present in store.

A scatter of early grasshopper beams (Renfrew, Newcastle-
upon-Tyne, Birmingham, Norwich and the Science Museum),
table engines (there is a fine Maudslay machine in the Science
Museum), oscillating cylinders (Norwich, Southampton) and
side-lever engines (such as the Napier engines in Kelvingrove
Museum, Glasgow, and on display in the new shopping precinct

at Dumbarton), survive in museums in various parts of the country, as do a considerable number of small horizontal engines. Such machines, where they survive, are now relatively certain of finding permanent homes. However, as the horizontal engine arrangement grew in size and complexity to serve the large mills and collieries of the late nineteenth century, they set ever-greater problems for their would-be preservers, because the sheer scale of these big engines makes removal an expensive operation, and it is usually not practicable to preserve them on site. A few survive, for the time being, due to the sympathy or affection of their owners – Courtaulds' retention of the magnificent Dee Mill engine is an outstanding example – and others have been moved to safety by the enthusiastic efforts of such bodies as the Northern Mill Engines Preservation Society and the University of Manchester Institute of Science and Technology Museum. Others, such as the engines at Abbey Lane, Leicester, have been incorporated in a museum of science and technology. Several large uniflow engines survive, but at present only the Galloway engine of 1924 in the Birmingham Museum of Science and Technology has been preserved. There is cause for concern that distinctive large engines should receive more attention, and that their preservation be supported by appropriate financial measures.

The problem of preservation is, if anything, even greater in the case of the large inverted vertical engines, such as the very efficient triple expansion engines installed in many waterworks late in the nineteenth century. Two of the huge engines installed by the Metropolitan Water Board at Kempton Park, London, as late as 1928, and made by Worthington Simpson, are still working and will probably be preserved. Among the last steam engines in regular textile-mill duty is a two-crank vertical compound engine built by Scott & Hodgson of Guide Bridge and still at work in Waterloo Mills (Taylor Bros. Ltd) at Silsden in Yorkshire. There are other mill engines still at work at Sutcliffe Clarksons Mills, Burnley; Jubilee Mills, Padiham; and Green's Mill, Whalley Bridge; but these are not inverted verticals. Chelvey engine, a disused pumping engine owned by Bristol Water Works, is an inverted vertical triple expansion engine which is likely to be preserved in conjunction with the Ironbridge Gorge Trust Museum because it is a Lilleshall engine. The Museum has also installed a large vertical blowing engine in an appropriate engine house on its Blist's Hill site. The prospects for most of the other remaining engines of this type, however, are not at the moment good, and some of them, like the two 1911 machines by Ashton Frost & Co. at Elkesley Pumping Station, Nottinghamshire, are at present under imminent threat of demolition. It is important that this most efficient type of reciprocating steam engine should be adequately represented in the stock of machines preserved for posterity in Britain.

Colliery steam winding engines have disappeared in large numbers in the last two decades. Some of these were vertical engines, such as the characteristic Durham vertical winder of which a specimen has been preserved in the North of England Open Air Museum at Beamish, having been moved from the coal mine on the adjoining site. But by far the most common arrangement for colliery winding was a horizontal engine, frequently with two engines side by side and the winding drum placed between them. Bristol City Museum managed to salvage such a machine from the Old Mills Colliery near Radstock, in the now abandoned North Somerset Coalfield, but the engine lies dismantled in the Museum store with no prospect of re-erection in the near future. Astley Green Colliery, near Manchester, has one of the largest winding engines ever built (by Yates & Thom) which, although now disused, will be preserved *in situ*. Scotland has a few steam winders still at work – the 'Lady Victoria' engine at Newtongrange Colliery, Midlothian, and the small private colliery in the far north of Sutherland at Brora.[3] A neat single-cylinder horizontal winder has been recently re-erected at Blist's Hill Museum and works under steam to demonstrate the pit-head operation of a typical small Shropshire coal mine. Considering the colossal service of the steam engine to the British coal industry, scant justice has been done to the memory of this service, and it is now probably too late to do much more.

In addition to the engines already mentioned in the collection of the Ironbridge Gorge Museum Trust at Blist's Hill, the Museum has also provided a home for large twin beam blowing engines which once provided blast for a local iron furnace, and these are among the few specimens to survive from the heavy iron and steel industry, the steam engines of which were normally very large (including the most powerful of all reciprocating steam engines, developing up to 25,000 hp) and subject to very hard service. They were also particularly vulnerable to the scrap-consumer, whose furnaces were too frequently adjacent to the engines when they became redundant. Two large rolling-mill engines survive, although very dilapidated, in the remains of the privately owned tinplate pack-mill at Kidwelly in South Wales, while better specimens are still in use at Beardmore's rolling mill in Glasgow.

Of the most modern steam engines, some Willans engines survive (there is a good specimen in the Science Museum), and a number of the thousands of high-speed forced-lubrication engines manufactured by Belliss & Morcom of Birmingham and other firms are still in service or maintained as stand-by units in institutions. Although of a size which can be much more easily accommodated than some of the large types of engine which we have been considering, it must be admitted that, except to the connoisseur, these engines have little visual appeal. But it is important that a few should be properly preserved in order to maintain a complete range of steam engines for inspection, and specimens have already been taken into care. Such engines, as they come out of commission, stand to gain from the awakening interest in the preservation of steam engines.

Marine steam engines, by the nature of their service, rarely survive the life of their ship, and few are available for examination except those preserved in the engine rooms of the few surviving vessels fitted with reciprocating steam engines. One such ship is the River Tyne tug *Reliant*, which has been installed in the new Neptune Hall at the National Maritime Museum, Greenwich, so that its engines can be seen. Perhaps the underwater archaeologist will eventually recover more of these marine steam engines: the greatest prize is probably the magnificent set of engines in the *Titanic* which have been on the sea bed since 1912, but the salvaging of these must await a technology beyond our present powers.

In determining priorities for preservation policy, it emerges from this review that too few reciprocating steam engines survive in Britain today to consider lightly the destruction of any further specimens, and that every case for preservation must be considered seriously and sympathetically. But in so far as comparative justice has been done to the different types, beam engines have fared reasonably well (although there are some serious gaps and deficiencies, such as the shortage of McNaughted engines); horizontal arrangements have done rather less well, but still not too badly, particularly the smaller designs; and inverted vertical, uniflow and modern high-speed arrangements least well. Preservationists should now concentrate on these latter types, although maintaining vigilance for the possibility of making up deficiencies in the national stock of the earlier types. The object should be to secure the preservation of a complete range of reciprocating steam engines in each of five or six large regions, which would make them reasonably accessible to everybody in the country while retaining plenty of scope for regional varieties and specialization according to particular manufacturers and the services performed by the engines. Left to themselves, it is probable that each museum and preservation society would concentrate on beam engines, because they are most immediately attractive, and the small engines (centrifugal pumps, bridge-swinging mechanisms, and such like) because they are the most simple to dismantle, store and present to public view. The fact that such bodies have hitherto been left to go about their collecting business in this way has led to many unbalanced and repetitive collections. This is not intended as a criticism of the curators and enthusiasts who have acquired these collections – often in the face of opposition, indifference, and grotesque lack of funds – as they have been forced to adopt a very empirical approach, taking such engines as they have been offered without the opportunity of being selective. Indeed, everybody concerned with the preservation of steam engines has every reason to be grateful to these pioneers, without whose efforts the position now would be almost hopeless. But the time has now arrived when it is both possible and necessary to adopt a more national attitude to the preservation of steam engines and, without breaking up any existing collections, to consider how they should be supplemented by items judiciously chosen in line with the sort of general priorities that we have been discussing.

We say that the time has come to take this broader view, not only because the stock of steam engines has dwindled alarmingly in the last few years and the wastage is still continuing, but also because there are encouraging signs that such an approach will now receive much more official support and encouragement than it has done previously. Such signs include a much greater readiness on the part of the Department of the Environment than existed only four or five years ago to apply the procedures of scheduling and listing in order to protect steam engines and their engine houses. Of course, as with any other monument, it is notorious that such statutory protection is in itself not enough to prevent an engine from rusting away or an engine house from falling into decay, but it does provide a vital underpinning for the efforts of enthusiasts who acquire from it a guarantee that their valuable maintenance work will not be wasted, and that engines, once protected, can be restored with the co-operation and under the supervision of the Ministry Inspectors. Another significant and welcome sign of greater official support for the preservation of steam engines comes from the creation of the new fund for the preservation of technological material distributed by the Department of Education and Science through the Science Museum. This makes money available, on a pound-for-pound basis, to provincial museums and preservation societies, for the removal and re-erection of artifacts, and it can be an enormous boon to bodies faced with an urgent need for cash in order to move a steam engine to safety. Again, as with statutory protection, there is no self-fulfilling ordinance here which will ensure that an engine, once moved, will be properly re-erected and preserved for posterity, but it is an important step in the right direction.

The problems of storage, of finding an appropriate building in which to re-erect an engine, whether it be an old engine house or a purpose-built modern museum, and of marshalling the skills necessary to perform the movement of the engine and its re-building, remain to be solved – but these are the perennial problems of museums and preservation societies. There is a particular poignancy about the last – the marshalling of necessary skills – because the number of engineers and mill-wrights familiar with steam engines is diminishing even more rapidly and irreversibly than the number of engines themselves. Dr Richard Hills, curator of the University of Manchester Institute of Science and Technology Museum, remarked recently that the successful removal and storage of several large engines undertaken by his museum has been the work of two highly skilled millwrights now approaching retirement, and that unless the engines can be reassembled while their skills are still available, he doubts whether it will be possible to put the pieces together again.[4] Such problems are common to all organizations concerned in the preservation of steam engines, but they should be seen against the background of greatly improved statutory protection and funding which make it possible for the first time to plan a national policy for preservation. The Council for British Archaeology Research Committee on Industrial Archaeology has now applied itself to this task and is preparing lists of steam engines distinguished according to the various priorities discussed above, on the basis of which recommendations for statutory protection are being made to the Department of the Environment. It is clearly not before time, but at least the task is now being tackled in a systematic fashion.

When it is not possible to preserve a steam engine it may be appropriate to make a model of it. Models have always been a valuable means of representing stationary steam engines, and some of the models have themselves become venerable objects of industrial archaeology, such as the model of the Newcomen engine on which Watt did the work leading to his invention of the separate condenser, preserved at the University of Glasgow. UMIST has recently undertaken the construction of a working replica one third the original size of the 1712 Newcomen engine, and this model has proved to be a very instructive teaching aid, illustrating vividly the operational problems of this type of engine.[5] Watt's own first model of his separate condenser is displayed in the Science Museum, which also has an excellent range of working models depicting every stage in the evolution of the steam engine. Considering the size of the great mill engines and their counterparts in the metal trades, coal mining, and marine engineering, it is likely that we will have to settle for models to illustrate many of them. But they should be regarded as a second best, and not as a complete substitute for the real-life machines which they portray.

Finally, a word about the international implications of this study of stationary steam engines. We have written primarily with British experience and British engines in mind, partly because this represents the limits of our own detailed field work, but mainly because the steam engine can be seen as the distinctive and outstanding British contribution to the process of world industrialization. Even though other countries copied and surpassed British achievements in steam technology, Britain remained the primary home of steam power and thus it does not seem necessary to excuse the British bias of this account. Nevertheless, the spread of steam technology to all parts of the world does mean that the implications of the industrial archaeological record of steam power need to be interpreted for the rest of the world. This, however, is a vast undertaking, and we will be happy to think that our study of the British precursors may stimulate other studies into the transfer and application of steam power elsewhere. In these pages we have only been able to hint at such world-wide implications, but we have no doubt that the increasing interest in the stationary reciprocating steam engine and its role in industrialization will lead to further work along these lines.

PART THREE

Gazetteer

List of Steam Engines

The following gazetteer does not attempt to give a comprehensive coverage of *all* surviving stationary steam engines. There are probably something like 600 of these in Britain at present, but not all of them are significant as industrial archaeological material, and consequently we have been selective. The principles of our selection have been:

1. To omit most post-1914 engines, unless there is some particular reason for including them.

2. To omit all engines which we know to have been destroyed or otherwise lost by January 1974. We realize that by the time the list is published many more will have gone, but we have tried to avoid anticipating this, so that our list is a reasonably complete survey of significant reciprocating stationary steam engines at the beginning of 1974. Where we are not certain about the fate of an engine we have tended to give it the benefit of the doubt.

3. To avoid individual listing of engines in museums, we have entered the main museums in the list, with a summary of the scope of their collection and a note on any outstanding specimens.

It has not proved possible to cross-check every reference in the list as closely as we would have liked to do, but we hope that industrial archaeologists will find it useful as it stands. Most of the material has been compiled from the Watkins Collection, but we have received valuable help in fixing such details as Grid References, and in arranging the information under the new administrative counties, from Martin Doughty, Colin Bowden, Keith Falconer, Judith Burchell and others.

Finally, it should be observed that the listing of an engine does not imply any right of access. Most of the engines remain, in fact, in private ownership, and it is much to be hoped that these owners, who deserve the gratitude of industrial archaeologists for the attention they have given to their steam engines, should not be given cause to regret their action by the importunity of enthusiasts. Most of the owners are glad to show their engines to genuine inquirers who take the trouble to make an appointment, but their right to discourage casual visitors must be respected.

137

AVON

Bath
ST 736 650
Stothert & Pitt Ltd.
Single-cylinder rotative beam engine.
Stothert & Pitt Ltd. 1866. Preserved.
12 in × 18 in: 50 psi.

Blagdon
ST 503 600
Bristol Waterworks Co.
Two Woolf compound rotative beam pumping engines.
Glenfield & Kennedy Ltd. 1902. Preserved.
21 in × 5 ft 2 in & 34 in × 7 ft: 17 rpm: 100 psi:
200 hp.

Bristol
City Museum, Queens Rd, Bristol 8.
A collection of engines, mostly in store, including
the twin-cylinder winding engine from Old Mills
Colliery, Somerset. Small bridge-raising engine from
Bathurst Basin, Bristol Docks, on display.

Bristol
ST 572 721
Underfall Yard Workshops, Port of Bristol Authority.
Horizontal twin-cylinder engine with belt drive to
machine shop.
Tangyes Ltd. 1885. Used occasionally.
8 in × 16 in: 60 rpm: 50 psi: 40 hp.

Bristol
ST 583 722
Prince's Wharf, City Docks.
Stationary heavy-lift wharf crane.
Stothert & Pitt. *c.* 1872/5. Disused.
Capable of 35-ton lift.

Bristol
ST 577 737
Victoria Pumping Station, Bristol Water Works Co.
Inverted vertical triple expansion engine.
Hathorn Davy & Co. Ltd. 1912. Disused.
16 in–28 in–46 in × 3 ft: 36 rpm: 160 psi: 250 hp.

Chelvey
ST 474 678
Bristol Water Works Co.
Inverted vertical triple expansion engine.
Lilleshall Co. 1923. Disused, likely to be preserved.
20 in–35 in–56 in × 3 ft 6 in: 22 rpm: 160 psi:
400 hp.

Weston-super-Mare
The Huish Collection.
An extensive private collection owned by Mr A. W. J.
Huish, Spring Palms, Church Road, Worle, Weston-
super-Mare. Mainly small engines, it includes the
horizontal tandem compound engine from the Pin
Mill at Charfield, Glos.

BEDFORDSHIRE

Bedford
Mander College of Further Education.
Woolf compound rotative beam pumping engine.
Goddard & Massey. 1878. Preserved.
18 in × 3 ft 8 in & 25 in × 5 ft 6 in: 16–20 rpm:
60 psi: ?100 hp.

BERKSHIRE

Pinkney's Green *Maidenhead Brick & Tile Co. Ltd.*
SU 864 832 Horizontal tandem compound engine.
Metcalfe. 1899. Derelict and partially dismantled.
Expected to be preserved at Wendron Forge, Cornwall.
12 in & 18 in × 2 ft: 100 rpm: 100 psi: 120 hp.

BUCKINGHAMSHIRE

Dancersend *Chiltern Springs Water Works, Bucks Water Board.*
SP 904 087 Twin single-cylinder rotative beam engine.
J. Kay. 1860 or '67. Preserved.
18 in × 2 ft 6 in: ?63 psi.

High Wycombe *The Thomas Glenister Co.*
SU 864 956 Horizontal tandem compound engine.
Davey, Paxman & Co. Ltd. Working.
12 in & 18 in × 1 ft 3 in: 220 rpm: 180 psi.

Compound semi-portable engine.
Marshall Sons & Co. 1878. Derelict.
9 in & 14 in × 1 ft 3 in.

CAMBRIDGESHIRE

Cambridge *Cheddars Lane Sewage Pumping Station.*
TL 465 593 Two horizontal tandem compound non-rotative pumping engines.
Hathorn Davey & Co. 1894. Preserved (Plate 9).
22 in & 44 in × 4 ft 0 in: 14 dspm: 100 psi.

Cambridge *Fleam Dyke Pumping Station, Cambridge Water Co.*
TL 540 549 Two horizontal tandem compound pumping engines.
Hathorn Davey. 1920. Working.
23 in & 51 in × 4 ft: 25 rpm: 120 psi.

Stretham *Waterbeach Level Drainage Commissioners.*
TL 517 730 Single-cylinder rotative beam engine and scoop wheel.
Butterley Co. 1831. Preserved (Plate 10).
39 in × 8 ft: 17 rpm: 5–10 psi: 70–80 hp.

CHESHIRE

Holmes Chapel *Flour Mill at Brereton*
SJ 757 677 Horizontal single-cylinder engine.
Fodens Ltd. Stopped work 1914. Preserved.
12 in × 2 ft: 80 rpm: ?60 psi: *c.* 30 hp.

Kettleshulme *Lumbhole Mill.*
SJ 988 804 Single-cylinder rotative beam engine.
Maker unknown. New cylinder supplied by J. & E. Armfield. Preserved.
21 in × 4 ft: ?35 rpm: ?30 psi: 50–60 hp.

Wincham
SJ 681 756
Lion Works.
Horizontal single-cylinder engine.
A. Lord. Brine pumping engine. Disused.

CLEVELAND

West
Hartlepool
NZ 522 339
Teesside & Hartlepool Port Authority.
Stationary wharf crane.
Cowan Sheldon. 1904. Disused, possibly to be scrapped. Two engines, one to rotate and one to raise and lower, by Westgarth of Hartlepool.
Maximum load 75 tons.

CORNWALL

Camborne
Holman Museum, Holman Bros Ltd, Camborne, Cornwall.
A private collection made by this famous engineering firm manufacturing engines and mining equipment. It includes a 22 in × 6 ft Cornish rotative beam pumping engine of 1851 from Rostowrack.

Helston
Wendron Forge Museum, Helston, Cornwall.
This is a new and enterprising collection of steam engines from all over the country, including West Ham and Bathford (Avon). But the main exhibit is a local engine – the 30 in × 9 ft Cornish beam pumping engine moved from the china-clay pit at Greensplat, near St Austell.

Pool
SW 675 417
East Pool and Agar Mine, Taylor's Shaft.
Cornish beam pumping engine.
Harvey & Co. 1892. Preserved.
90 in × 10 ft: 5 spm: 45 psi: 425 hp.

Pool
SW 674 415
East Pool and Agar Mine, East Pool.
Cornish rotative beam winding engine.
Holman Bros. 1887. Preserved.
30 in × 9 ft.

Pool
SW 668 412
East Pool and Agar Mine, South Crofty.
Cornish beam pumping engine.
Sandys, Vivian & Co. 1854. Preserved.
80 in × 10 ft: 11½ spm: 40 psi: 335 hp.

St Dennis
SW 945 568
Parkandillack Clayworks.
Cornish beam pumping engine.
Sandys, Vivian & Co. 1852. Preserved.
50 in × 10 ft.

St Just
SW 368 345
Levant Mine.
Cornish rotative beam winding engine.
Harvey & Co. 1840. Preserved.
24 in × 4 ft.

St Stephen SW 947 552	*Goonvean Clayworks.* Cornish beam pumping engine. Harvey & Co. 1863. Disused. 50 in × 10 ft.

CUMBRIA

Cockermouth NY 120 307	*Jennings Bros Ltd, Castle Brewery.* Single-cylinder vertical engine. *c.* 1856. Disused. Horizontal single-cylinder engine. Robey & Co. Ltd. On stand-by.
Silloth	*Carrs Flour Mills Ltd, Solway Mills, Silloth.* Horizontal cross compound engine. S.A. des Ateliers Carels Frères. 1904. Working. 24½ in & 37⅝ in × 4 ft 11 in: 65 rpm: 160 psi: 700 hp.
Whitehaven NX 967 176	*Haig Pit.* Two horizontal twin-cylinder winding engines. Bever, Dorling & Co. Ltd. *c.* 1917 and ?. Working. 30 in × 5 ft and 40 in × 7 ft: 40 rpm: 120 psi.
Workington	*Workington Iron & Steel Co.* Horizontal twin-cylinder engine. Davey Bros. 1890s. 32 in × 4 ft: 70 rpm: 180 psi: 1,700 hp.

DERBYSHIRE

Bamford SK 205 834	*Carbolite Ltd.* Horizontal tandem compound. J. Musgrave & Son. 1907. Preserved, workable (Plate 23). 16 in & 30 in × 2 ft 6 in: 103 rpm: 160 psi: 400 hp.
Cadley Hill SK 278 192	*Cadley Hill Colliery.* Horizontal twin-cylinder winding engine. Thornewill & Warham. 1868. Working. 24 in × 4 ft: 32 rpm: 80 psi.
Cromford SK 315 557	*Cromford Canal Pump House.* Cornish beam pumping engine. Graham & Co. 1849. Preserved. 36 in × 8 ft 6 in.
Hartington SK 170 608	*D.S.F. Refractories Ltd.* Horizontal twin-cylinder engine. Robey & Co. 1905. Working.
Heath SK 427 665	*Williamthorpe Colliery.* Horizontal twin-cylinder winding engine. Markham & Co. Ltd. 1904. Derelict, to be scrapped. 42 in × 7 ft: 30 rpm: 130 psi.

Killamarsh   *Westhorpe Colliery.*
SK 453 797   Horizontal twin-cylinder winding engine.
                    Robey & Co. Ltd? Rebuilt by Robey in 1924. Work-
                    ing.

Mansfield   *Pleasley Colliery.*
SK 498 644   Horizontal twin-cylinder winding engine.
                    Lilleshall Co. 1902. Working.
                    28 in × 6 ft: 30 rpm: 80 psi.

                    Horizontal twin-cylinder winding engine.
                    Markham & Co. 1924. Working.
                    36 in × 6 ft: 140 psi.

Middleton   *Middleton Incline, Cromford & High Peak Railway.*
SK 275 552   Double single-cylinder beam winding engine.
                    Butterley Co. 1825. Preserved.
                    26 in × 5 ft: 30 rpm: 5–10 psi.

Woodville   *J. Knowles & Co.*
SK 312 184   Two horizontal single-cylinder engines.
                    Buxton & Thornley, *c.* 1900 or earlier. Disused, one
                    likely to be scrapped.

                    DEVON

Dartmouth   *The Newcomen Society.*
SX 878 514   One of the few surviving Newcomen engines, moved
                    from Hawksbury (Warwicks) in 1966 and preserved
                    in the home-town of its inventor. Probably dating
                    from mid-eighteenth century but subsequently modi-
                    fied.
                    22 in × *c.* 4 ft: 6 hp.

Exeter   *Maritime Museum, The Quay, Exeter EX2 4AN.*
                    The collection of small craft includes some steam-
                    powered boats. Of special interest is the scraper-
                    dredger made about 1844 from designs by I. K. Brunel
                    and serving in Bridgwater Docks until these closed
                    in 1970.

Uffculme   *Fox Bros Spinning Mill, Coldharbour.*
ST 062 122   Horizontal cross compound engine.
                    Pollit & Wigzell Ltd. 1910. Working.
                    13 in & 26 in × 3 ft: 90 rpm: 135 psi: 320 hp.

                    DORSET

Blandford   *Hall & Woodhouse, Brewery.*
St Mary   Horizontal single-cylinder engine.
ST 886 058   Gimson & Co. 1899. Working.
                    12 in × 2 ft: 100 rpm: 75 psi: *c.* 25 hp.

Bridport
SY 466 922

J. C. & R. H. Palmer.
Inverted vertical single-cylinder engine.
Brown & May. Working.
c. 9 in × 1 ft: 100 rpm: 100 psi: 10 hp.

Poole

Technical College, North Rd.
Horizontal cross compound engine.
Wren & Hopkinson. 1880s. Ex Sydenham's Sawmill, Poole.
10 in & 18 in × 2 ft: 90 rpm: 80 psi: 60–70 hp.

Weymouth
SY 681 786

Devenish Weymouth Brewery Ltd.
Horizontal single-cylinder engine.
Barrett, Exall & Andrews. Preserved.
11 in × 1 ft 3 in.

DURHAM

Cold Hesledon
NZ 411 469

Sunderland and South Shields Water Co.
Two Cornish beam pumping engines.
Davy Brothers Ltd. 1879. Disused.
72 in × 9 ft: 6–8 spm: 40 psi.

Darlington
NZ 254 139

Darlington Water Works, Coniscliffe Rd.
Woolf compound beam pumping engine.
Teesdale Bros. 1904. Disused, but could be worked.
c. 18 in × 5 ft 6 in & 29 in × 7 ft: 10–12 rpm: 100 psi: 100 hp.

Neasham
NZ 332 111

Fox, Lane & Co. Ltd.
Horizontal single-cylinder engine.
Tangyes Ltd. 1878. Derelict.

ESSEX

Ilford
TQ 433 863

Ilford Pumping Station, Essex Water Co.
Inverted vertical triple expansion pumping engine.
Hathorn, Davey & Co. 1906. Disused.

Langford
TL 835 090

Langford Pumping Station, Essex Water Co.
Inverted vertical triple expansion pumping engine.
Lilleshall. *c.* 1930. Preserved.

Maldon

Beeleigh Mill, Green Bros.
Woolf compound beam engine.
Wentworth. 1845.
c. 12 in × 2 ft 6 in & 15 in × 3 ft 4 in: 25 rpm: 30 psi: 40 hp.

Orsett
TL 633 618

H. C. Bridgers Mill, Baker St.
A-frame beam engine.
In dilapidated condition, minus beam.

GLOUCESTERSHIRE

Stroud
SO 886 023

St Mary's Mill, Chalford.
Horizontal side-by-side compound engine.
Tangyes Ltd.
13 in & 25 in × 2 ft: 90 rpm: 120 psi: ?150 hp.

HAMPSHIRE

Havant

Havant Pumping Station, Portsmouth Water Works.
Grasshopper beam engine.
Easton, Amos & Anderson. c. 1860. Preserved.
12 in × 1 ft 4 in.

Portsmouth
SZ 675 989

Eastney Sewage Pumping Station.
Two Woolf compound rotative beam pumping engines.
J. Watt & Co. 1887. Preserved.
20 in × 4 ft 6 in & 30 in × 6 ft: 18–24 rpm: 60 psi:
150 hp.

Southampton

Maritime Museum, Wool Hall, Bridge St, Southampton.
Contains steam engines from marine services. Of
special interest is the oscillating engine from the
paddle steamer *Empress* (Plate 14).

Southwick
SU 627 085

Golden Lion Home Brewery.
Horizontal single-cylinder engine.
Maker and date unknown. To be preserved as whole
plant.
6 in × 10 in: 120 rpm: 80 psi: 10 hp.

Twyford
SU 492 248

Pumping Station, Southampton Water Works Dept.
Inverted vertical triple expansion pumping engine.
Hathorn, Davey & Co. 1913. Possibly not installed
until 1916. Disused; trust to be formed for preservation of entire complex.
17 in–27 in–46 in × 3 ft: 25 rpm: 160 psi.

Winchester

*County Museum Service, Hants., Chilcomb House, Bar
End, Winchester.*
The Tasker Collection, containing items from the
agricultural machinery firm of Taskers of Andover,
is at present in store here. It is not yet accessible to
the public. The collection includes several steam engines, such as a horizontal single-cylinder engine of
10 hp.

HEREFORD AND WORCESTER

Hereford
SO 496 393

Broomy Hill Pumping Station, Hereford Water Board.
Inverted vertical triple expansion pumping engine.
Worth Mackenzie & Co. 1895. Preserved.
c. 13½ in–21¼ in–36 in × 2 ft 6 in.

Bourne End
TZ 019 061

J. W. Ward & Son.
Horizontal tandem compound engine.
Davey, Paxman & Co. Installed 2nd-hand 1926.
Working.

Turnford
TL 360 044

Pumping Station, Metropolitan Water Board.
Side-lever engine.
Boulton & Watt. 1845. Compounded by addition of
inverted vertical single-cylinder engine. R. Moreland
& Son. 1882. Preserved.
28 in × 3 ft 6 in: 15 rpm: 5–10 psi: 90 hp.

HUMBERSIDE

Cottingham
TA 047 342

Pumping Station, Hull Corp. Water Dept.
Three inverted vertical triple expansion pumping
engines.
Worthington Simpson. 1930. Expected to be superseded, one to be preserved.

Kingston-
upon-Hull
TA 042 295

Springhead Pumping Station, Hull Corp. Water Dept.
Cornish beam pumping engine.
Bells, Lightfoot. 1876. Preserved (Plate 2).
90 in × 11 ft: 12 spm: 40 psi: 300 hp.

Newport
SE 854 308

Newport Brick Works.
Horizontal single-cylinder engine.
Robey & Co. 1909. Working.

ISLE OF WIGHT

East Cowes

Coles Shipyard, Shamblers Hard, East Cowes.
Grasshopper beam engine. Slipway haulage.

Newport
SZ 489 899

Mr Taylor, Albany Farm, Albany Rd.
Grasshopper beam engine.
Easton & Amos. *c.* 1870s. ?ex Osborne House.

Horizontal single-cylinder engine.
Pollit & Wigzell. *c.* 1900. Ex Sawmill.
c. 12 in × 1 ft 6 in.

KENT

Ashford
TR 019 428

Henwood Pumping Station, Mid Kent Water Co.
Two Woolf compound rotative beam pumping engines.
Thomas Horn. *c.* 1870 & 1881. Preserved (**Plate 15**).
8 in × 1 ft 6 in & 14 in × 2 ft 3 in.

Single-cylinder vertical engine.
Preserved.
c. 4½ in × 6 in.

Crossness
TQ 484 811

Sewage Treatment Works G.L.C.
Four rotative beam pumping engines.
J. Watt. 1865. Converted to triple expansion by Goodfellows, 1899. Preserved (Plate 6).
19 in & 32 in × 6 ft 10½ in & 44 in × 9 ft: 10½ rpm:
30 psi: 210 hp.

Dover
TR 322 422

Waterworks, Folkestone & District Water Co.
Two inverted vertical triple expansion engines.
Worthington Simpson. 1939. Working.
c. 14 in–24 in–36 in × 3 ft: 21 rpm: 185 psi.

Faversham

Shepherd Neame Brewery, 17 Court St, Faversham.
Two horizontal single-cylinder engines.
One by Tangyes, the other unknown.
12 in × 2 ft 6 in: 80 rpm: 100 psi: 30 hp.

Folkestone
TR 210 380

*Upper Cherry Garden Water Works, Folkestone &
District Water Co.*
Two (Worthington) horizontal twin tandem triple
expansion non-rotative pumping engines.
James Simpson. 1889. Preserved.
c. 8 in–10 in–16½ in × 1 ft 3 in.

Single-cylinder vertical steeple engine.
Pre-1870? Preserved.
c. 7½ in × 1 ft.

Also a vertical two-cylinder donkey engine.
Ex Lower Standen. F. & D. Water Co. Pre-1880.
Preserved.

Sevenoaks

Kentish White Brick Co., Borough Green Rd, Ightham.
Single-cylinder horizontal engine.
Robey. Working.

LANCASHIRE

Barnoldswick
SD 875 461

J. Nutter & Sons Ltd.
Horizontal cross compound engine.
Wm Roberts & Sons. 1922. Working.
c. 16 in & 32 in × 4 ft: 68 rpm: 160 psi: 600 hp.
Horizontal single-cylinder engine.
Brown, Son & Pickles. 1914. Working.
8 in × 1 ft: 120 rpm: 60–80 psi: 10 hp.

Burnley
SD 835 327

Sutcliffe & Clarkson Ltd.
Horizontal cross compound engine.
W. & J. Yates? *c.* 1890. Working.
16 in & 30 in × 3 ft: 60 rpm: 140 psi: 350 hp.

Church
SD 741 287

W. & F. Chambers Ltd, Indian & Primrose Mill.
Horizontal cross compound engine.
Ashton, Frost & Co. 1884. Working.
17½ in & 36½ in × 4 ft 6 in: 42 rpm: 150 psi: 350 hp.

Clitheroe	*J. Thornber Ltd, Holme Mill.* Horizontal cross compound engine. Clayton & Goodfellows. 1910. 15 in & 30 in × 2 ft 6 in: 66 rpm: 100 psi: 350 hp.
Darwen SD 696 220	*J. Grime Ltd, Sunnybank Mill.* Vertical single-cylinder engine. Possibly by Rishton Foundry. 1850s? Disused. Possibly removed for preservation.
Darwen	*Nr India Mill, Darwen.* Horizontal cross compound engine. J. & E. Wood. 1900s. Preserved in open (Plate 20). 16 in & 32 in × 3 ft 6 in: 75 rpm: 120 psi: 450 hp.
Harle Syke SD 868 348	*Queen St Manufacturing Co. Ltd.* Horizontal tandem compound engine. Wm Roberts & Sons. 1875. Working. 16 in & 32 in × 4 ft: 80 rpm: 130 psi: 500 hp.
Harle Syke SD 867 349	*H. & J. Crowther Ltd.* Horizontal tandem compound engine. Pollit & Wigzell Ltd. 1905. Working. 17 in & 35 in × 4 ft: 80 rpm: 150 psi: 700 hp.
Haslingden SD 790 229	*Grane Mfrg Co., W. & J. Baldwin Ltd.* Horizontal cross compound engine. S. S. Stott & Co. 1907. Working. 18 in & 36 in × 4 ft: 61 rpm: 130 psi: *c.* 600 hp.
Haslingden SD 791 221	*J. S. Slater Ltd.* Horizontal tandem compound engine. S. S. Stott & Co. *c.* 1900. Working. 16 in & 32 in × 3 ft: 80 rpm: 160 psi: 250 hp.
Helmshore SD 780 210	*Higher Mill, Helmshore.* Beam engine. Peel, Williams & Peel. 1846. Preserved.
Nelson SD 869 388	*Cooper & Derbyshire Ltd, Lee Bank Mill.* Horizontal cross compound engine. Wm Roberts & Sons. 1914. Preserved.
Padiham SD 797 333	*Padiham Room & Power Co.* Horizontal cross compound engine. W. & J. Yates, Blackburn. 1888. Working. 21 in & 42 in × 5 ft: 56 rpm: 140 psi: 800 hp. Three horizontal single-cylinder engines. 1. S. Baldwin & Heap. *c.* 1880. 2 & 3. S. Baldwin, possibly later. One working, two idle.

F

Whalley
SD 723 357

Green Bros Ltd.
Horizontal cross compound engine.
W. & J. Yates. *c.* 1885–88. Working.
16 in & 30 in × 4 ft: 55 rpm: 100 psi: 350 hp.

Wigan

Trencherfield Mill, Courtaulds Ltd, Northern Textile Division, Wallgate.
Horizontal twin tandem triple expansion engine.
J. & E. Wood. 1907. Preserved, possibly to be made workable.
25⅛ in–40⅛ in & 2 ft × 44¼ in × 5 ft: 67¾ rpm: 200 psi: 2,500 hp.

LEICESTERSHIRE

Bagworth
SK 460 068

Desford Colliery.
Two horizontal twin-cylinder winding engines.
Wood & Gee. 1901. Working, scheduled for replacement 1974.
26 in × 4 ft 6 in: 30 rpm: 100 psi.

Donisthorpe
SK 313 143

Colliery.
Horizontal twin-cylinder winding engine.
Maker unknown. Working.
26 in × 4 ft 6 in: 35 rpm: 120 psi.

Leicester
SK 589 067

Leicester Museum & Art Gallery, Abbey Lane Sewage Works Industrial Museum.
Four compound rotative beam pumping engines.
Gimson & Co. 1891. Preserved (Plate 8).
30 in × 5 ft 9 in & 48 in × 8 ft 6 in: 12 rpm: 80 psi: 200 hp.

Horizontal twin-cylinder winding engine.
Handyside. From Morton Colliery. 1865 (Plate 16).
30 in × 5 ft: 28 rpm: 65 psi.

Loughborough

Loughborough University of Technology.
Single-cylinder beam engine.
Watt. Preserved in grounds.
24 in × 3 ft: 16–18 rpm: 25 psi: 17·6 hp.

Moira
SK 313 163

Rawdon Colliery.
Horizontal twin-cylinder winding engine.
1868, rebuilt 1913. Working.
27 in × 5 ft: 40 rpm: 90 psi.

LINCOLNSHIRE

Lincoln

Museum of Lincolnshire Life, Lincs Assoc. County Centre, Burton Rd, Lincoln.
This Lincolnshire Association collection contains examples of steam engines from local engineering firms such as Ruston-Proctor, Ruston & Hornsby, and Robey.

Sleaford
TF 074 452

Hewitt Bros.
Two horizontal tandem compound engines.
Robey & Co. *c.* 1904. Disused.
c. 18 in & 27 in × 2 ft 6 in: 100 rpm: 150 psi: 150 hp.

Spalding Marsh
TF 262 262

Pinchbeck Marsh Pumping Station.
Single-cylinder rotative beam pumping engine with scoop wheel. Maker unknown. 1833. Preserved.
25¾ in × 4 ft 6 in: 25 rpm: 15 psi: 25 hp.

Stamford
TF 028 071

Melbourn Bros Ltd
Inverted vertical single-cylinder engine.
Marshall. *c.* 1910. Working.
c. 10 in × 1 ft: 100 rpm: 80 psi: 12 hp.

Tattershall
TF 206 558

Dogdyke Pumping Station, Witham 3rd District Internal Drainage Board.
Single-cylinder rotative beam engine and scoop wheel.
Maker unknown. 1855. To be preserved.
24 in × 3 ft 6 in: 18–20 spm: 10 psi: ?50 hp.

LONDON (Greater London Council)

Kempton Park
TQ 110 708

Metropolitan Water Board, Pumping Station.
Five inverted vertical triple expansion pumping engines.
Lilleshall Co. 1906. Disused.
1 & 2: 13 in–21 in–32 in × 4 ft: 25 rpm: 150 psi: 100 hp. 3, 4 & 5: 21 in–34 in–52 in × 4 ft: 25 rpm: 150 psi: 273 hp.

Two inverted vertical triple expansion pumping engines.
Worthington Simpson. 1928. Working.
29 in–54 in–86 in × 5 ft 6 in: 24 rpm: 200 psi: 1,000 hp.

Two inverted vertical compound engines.
Ashworth & Parker. 1927. Disused.
9 in & 13 in × 5 in: 450 rpm: 150 psi.
10 in & 15 in × 6 in: 450 rpm: 150 psi.
Inverted vertical compound engine.
W. H. Allen Sons. 1930. Workable.
8 in & 14 in × 6½ in: 475 rpm: 150 psi: *c.* 84 hp.

Kew Bridge
TQ 188 780

Metropolitan Water Board, Pumping Station.
Five Cornish Pumping Engines.

The 'West Cornish' beam engine.
Boulton & Watt. 1820, converted to Cornish principle 1848. Preserved.
64 in × 8 ft: 8–10 spm: 40 psi: 90 hp.

Beam engine.
Maudslay Sons & Field. 1838. Preserved.
64 in × 8 ft: 8–10 spm: 40 psi: 125 hp.

The 'Grand Junction' beam engine.
Sandys, Carne & Vivian. 1845. Preserved (Plate 1).
90 in × 11 ft: 8 spm: 40 psi: 400 hp.

Bull engine.
Harvey & Co. 1856–9. Preserved.
70 in × 10 ft: 8–10 spm: 40 psi: 160 hp.

Beam engine.
Harvey & Co. 1869. Preserved.
100 in × 11 ft: 6–8 spm: 50 psi: 411 hp.

Littleton
TQ 060 696

Metropolitan Water Board, Pumping Station.
Two uniflow engines.
Worthington Simpson. 1924. Disused.
28 in × 3 ft 3 in: 140 spm: 195 psi: 750 hp.

Science Museum

Exhibition Rd, South Kensington, London SW7.
This is the outstanding collection of steam technology
in Britain. It contains an extensive range of full-size
engines from early Newcomen types through to steam
turbines, and including a Boulton & Watt rotative
action beam engine with sun and planet gearing
which is regularly operated by compressed air. There
is also a very large selection of models of steam engines,
and other features of ancillary interest such as James
Watt's workshop, which was moved from Birmingham and reconstructed in the Museum.

Tottenham
TQ 344 888

*Markfield Rd Sewage Pumping Station, Haringey
Borough.*
Woolf compound rotative beam pumping engine.
Wood Bros. 1886. Preserved.
c. 21 in × 4 ft 4 in & 36 in × 6 ft: 18 rpm: 120 psi.

Tower Bridge
TQ 337 802

Corporation of London.
Two horizontal twin tandem pumping engines.
Armstrong, Mitchell. 1894. Preserved.
18 in & 30 in × 3 ft: 50 rpm: 80 psi: *c.* 300 hp.

Horizontal cross compound pumping engine.
Vickers, Armstrong. 1941. Disused.
c. 18 in & 30 in × 2 ft 3 in: 50 rpm: 80 psi: 150 hp.

Walton
TQ 118 684

Pumping Station, Metropolitan Water Board.
Inverted vertical triple expansion pumping engine.
Thames Ironworks. 1911. On stand-by.
14 in–23 in–38 in × 2 ft 6 in: 132 rpm: 195 psi: 600
hp.

Inverted vertical triple expansion pumping engine.
Davey & Co. 1924. Working.
25 in–47 in–70 in × 5 ft: 20 rpm: 200 psi: 700 hp.

Wandsworth
TQ 256 747

Ram Brewery, Young & Co.
Two Woolf compound rotative beam engines.
Wentworth & Sons. 1835 and 1867. Working.
c. 9 in × 2 ft 6 in & 15 in × 3 ft 6 in: 32 rpm: 16 hp.

Whitechapel
TQ 348 819

Albion Brewery, Watney Mann Ltd.
Single-cylinder rotative beam engine.
Kittoe & Brotherhood. 1867. Preserved.
28 in × 4 ft 6 in.

Single-cylinder horizontal engine.
Robert Morton. 1872. Preserved.
24 in × 3 ft 6 in.

MANCHESTER (Greater Manchester)

Bolton

Bolton, Lancs, Planning Dept.
Vertical single-cylinder engine (from **Low Bentham Silk Mill**). Hick, Hargreaves. 1886. Preserved. A proposal to re-erect it somewhere in the town precinct has now been accepted.
24 in × 2 ft 6 in: 88 rpm: 120 psi: 120 hp.

Bolton
SD 715 083

T. Walmsley & Sons.
Horizontal single-cylinder engine, driving rolling mill.
Working.
27 in × 4 ft: 30 rpm: 70 psi: 250 hp.

Two inverted single-cylinder engines.
Hick, Hargreaves & Co. Installed 1921, working.
21 in × 3 ft: 60 rpm: 70 psi: *c.* 250 hp.

Hollinwood

Ferranti Ltd.
Inverted vertical cross compound engine.
Ferranti. 1898. Preserved.
13 in & 28 in × 1 ft 1 in: 120 rpm: 120 psi: 350 hp.

Leigh
SD 650 006

Parsonage Colliery.
Horizontal twin-cylinder winding engine.
W. & J. Galloway. 1923. Working.
40 in × 6 ft: 30 rpm: 140 psi.

Horizontal twin-cylinder winding engine.
Markham & Co. 1920. Working.
40 in × 7 ft.

Leigh
SJ 631 999

Bickershaw Colliery.
Horizontal twin-cylinder winding engine.
J. Wood. 1880s. Working.
36 in × 6 ft: 40 rpm: 100 psi.

Horizontal twin-cylinder winding engine.
Walker Bros. 1881. Working.
32 in × 7 ft: 100 psi.

Littleborough
SD 943 164

A. &. W. Law Ltd.
Horizontal single-cylinder engine.
Earnshaw & Holt. 1864. Derelict.
28 in × 4 ft: 63 rpm: 90 psi: 250 hp.

Manchester

*Museum of Science and Technology, 97 Grosvenor St,
Manchester M1 7HF.*
A representative selection of engines covering the main
phases of steam technology, with the Newcomen type
represented by a working replica constructed to $\frac{1}{3}$
the original size from a drawing of 1719 by Barney.
The Haydock single-cylinder beam engine of 1863,
but probably modified from an earlier engine, is at
present in store. There is also a collection of archives
from some prominent local engineering firms.

Norden
SD 852 148

R. Cudworth Ltd.
Horizontal tandem compound engine.
S. S. Stott & Co. 1895. Preserved, workable.
c. 12 in & 24 in × 2 ft 6 in: 100 rpm: 140 psi: 150
hp.

Rochdale

*Northern Mill Engine Society, 2 Brocklebank Rd,
Rochdale, Lancs.*
The Society is engaged in removing and storing steam
engines from mills in Lancashire and Yorkshire in
order to ensure their preservation. Most of the engines
saved are at present dismantled and in store, but it is
hoped to prepare them for exhibition in a museum.
They include some beam engines, of which one has
been McNaughted – specifications: 20 in × 3 ft &
28 in × 6 ft: 45 rpm: 100 psi: 250 hp.

Rochdale
SD 887 111

Ensor Mill Ltd.
Horizontal cross compound engine.
Yates & Thom Ltd. 1915. Working, due to close.
19 in & 40 in × 4 ft: 73 rpm: 165 psi: *c.* 600 hp.

Horizontal tandem compound engine.
Wm Sharples. 1908. Working, due to close.
15½ in & 39 in × 4 ft: 72½ rpm: 165 psi: 565 hp.

Rochdale

*J. Holroyd & Co., Gear Engineers, 108 Manchester
Rd.*
Single-cylinder beam engine.
Petrie. 1841. Re-erected from Whitelees Mill, Little-
borough.
25½ in × 5 ft: 34 rpm: 40 psi: 125 hp.

Rochdale

A. & W. Law & Co., Smallbridge.
Inverted vertical single-cylinder engine.
Hindley.
3 in × 5 in: 120 rpm: 100 psi.

Royton
SD 929 081

Hardman & Ingham Ltd.
Inverted vertical compound engine.
Scott & Hodgson. 1912. Disused, future uncertain,
still workable.
14 in & 30 in × 2 ft 6 in: 90 rpm: 160 psi: 250 hp.

Saddleworth

Saddleworth Woollen Co., Valley Mills, Delph.
Horizontal tandem compound engine.
Broadbent. 1899. Disused 1970, *in situ*,
18 in & 29 in × 3 ft 6 in: 80 rpm: 160 psi: 500 hp.

Salford

*Science Museum, Buile Mill Park, Eccles Old Rd,
Pendleton, Salford M6 8GL.*
No general collection of steam engines, but has a
vertical engine from a local firm, where it drove engraving machinery.

Shaw
SD 944 091

Dee Mill, Courtaulds Ltd.
Horizontal twin tandem compound engine.
Scott & Hodgson. 1907. Preserved (Plate 22).
18½ & 44 in × 5 ft: 60 rpm: 160 psi: 1,500 hp.

Shaw
SD 939 093

Sutcliffe, Speakman & Co.
Horizontal twin tandem compound engine.
Buckley & Taylor. 1884. Disused, shaft broken.
22 in & 44 in × 6 ft: 54 rpm: 150 psi: *c.* 1,200 hp.

Tyldesley
SJ 705 999

Astley Green Colliery.
Horizontal twin tandem compound winding engine.
Yates & Thom. 1912. Preserved.
35 in & 60 in × 6 ft: 20 rpm: 150 psi: ?3,000 hp.

MERSEYSIDE

Birkenhead
SJ 327 891

Shore Road Station.
Compound grasshopper beam pump.
Barclay. Preserved.
36 in × 10 ft & 55 in × 13 ft: 6–8 spm: 70 psi.

Birkenhead
SJ 325 900

Wallasey Dock.
Two inverted vertical single tandem engines.
Gwynne. 1889.
22 in & 42 in × 2 ft 6 in: 90 rpm: 120 psi: 475 hp.

Liverpool

*City of Liverpool Museums, William Brown St,
Liverpool L3 8EN.* There is a large and important
collection of ship models at this museum, including
many steam ships.

Sutton Manor
SJ 518 908

Sutton Manor Colliery.
Horizontal cross compound winding engine.
Fraser & Chalmers. 1907. Working.
? × 5 ft: 150 psi.

Horizontal cross compound winding engine.
Yates & Thom. 1914. Working.
c. 28 in & 52 in × 5 ft: 45 rpm: 150 psi.

MIDLANDS (West Midlands)

Birmingham

Museum of Science & Industry, Newhall St, Birmingham B3 1RZ.
This museum has one of the best collections illustrating steam technology in Britain. It includes specimens of most main types and from most phases of development, and has facilities for demonstrating some of them occasionally in steam. Among the more interesting exhibits are an Amos beam engine of 1864, a Pollit & Wigzell horizontal tandem Corliss engine of 1909, a Willans central-valve engine (one of the few of this important type to have been preserved), and a Galloway uniflow engine of 1924. The collection is currently being re-housed in a new museum building.

Birmingham
SP 077 883

Aston Expressway, Gravelly Hill interchange.
Beam blowing engine. Permanent display on the Dartmouth Concourse. Boulton & Watt. 1817.

Brownhills
SK 039 053

The Potters Clay & Coal Co.
Horizontal single-cylinder engine.
Tangyes. 1896. Working.
20 in × 3 ft: 85 rpm: 120 psi: *c.* 100 hp.

Dudley
SO 949 917

The Black Country Museum.
This museum, at the junction of the Tipton Road and the Birmingham to Wolverhampton trunk road (A4123), and near to Dudley Castle and the north portal of the Dudley Canal tunnel, is due to open soon. It includes several interesting steam engines.

NORFOLK

Marham
TF 717 107

Wisbech & District Water Board.
Two horizontal twin tandem triple expansion non-rotative pumping engines.
Worthington Simpson. 1938. Working.
12 in–19 in–30 in × 2 ft: 33 rpm: 150 psi: 190 hp.

One inverted vertical compound engine (enclosed).
A. Dodman & Co. Workable.
c. 9 in & 18 in × 1 ft 6 in: 60 psi: 25 hp.

Norwich
City of Norwich Museums.
The headquarters are at the Castle Museum, Norwich, NOR 65B, but there are also technological exhibits at the Bridewell Museum, Bridewell Alley, St Andrew's St, Norwich NOR 02H. Steam engines of interest include the beam engine from Baggs' Brewery (*c.* 1840) (Plate 18), a grasshopper engine (dismantled, in store), and two small oscillating engines (Plate 19).

West Newton
TF 707 273
Appleton Pumping Station.
Single-cylinder horizontal engine.
Pratchitt Bros. 1877. Disused, possibly to be preserved.

NORTHAMPTONSHIRE

Little Houghton
SP 804 605
Rousselot Gelatine Ltd.
Horizontal single-cylinder engine.
Piguet, Lyon-Anzin. 1928. On stand-by.
19 in × 2 ft 4 in: 90 rpm: 140 psi: 50 hp.

Northampton
SP 764 603
Cliftonville Waterworks, Mid Northamptonshire Water Board.
Compound rotative beam pumping engine.
Easton & Amos. 1863. Preserved, in store.
15 in × 3 ft 9 in & 30 in × 5 ft: 20 rpm.

Stoke Bruerne
The Waterways Museum, near Towcester, Northants NN12 7SE.
Devoted entirely to the history of inland waterways, the collection includes a vertical steam engine built by George Farrin of Bromsgrove in 1890 for the canal barge *Sabrina.*

NORTHUMBERLAND

Ashington
NZ 289 884
Woodhorn Colliery.
Horizontal twin-cylinder winding engine.
Grant Ritchie. 1900. Working.
28 in × 6 ft: 35 rpm: 100 psi.

NOTTINGHAMSHIRE

Bestwood
SK 557 475
Bestwood Colliery.
Vertical twin-cylinder winding engine.
Poss. Worsley Mesnes. *c.* 1875? Preserved.
36 in × 6 ft: 18 rpm: 80 psi: 1,200 hp.

Bilsthorpe
SK 653 615
Bilsthorpe Colliery.
Horizontal twin-cylinder winding engine.
Markham & Co. 1926. Working.

Horizontal twin-cylinder winding engine.
Thornewill & Warham. 1888. Working.

F*

Elkesley
SK 664 760

Elkesley Pumping Station.
Two inverted vertical triple expansion pumping
engines.
Ashton, Frost. 1911. Working until 1973, when one
was damaged in an accident.
26 in–45 in–68 in × 4 ft: 24 rpm: 180 psi: 300 hp.

Kirkby-in-
Ashfield
SK 474 551

Langton Colliery.
Horizontal twin-cylinder winding engine.
Robey. 1914. Working.
39 rpm.

Horizontal twin-cylinder engine.
Robert Daglish. 1925. Working.
26 in × 5 ft: 40 rpm: 110 psi.

Kirkby-in
Ashfield
SK 488 550

Bentinck Colliery.
Three horizontal twin-cylinder winding engines.
1. J. Warner. 1890. Working, prob. not installed here
   until 1915.
   36 in × 5 ft: 25 rpm: 100 psi.

2. R. Daglish. 1890. Working.
   30 in × 6 ft: 25–30 rpm: 120 psi.

3. Grange Iron Co. Installed 2nd-hand 1890. Working.
   40 in × 6 ft: ?20 rpm: 120 psi.

Linby
SK 535 505

Linby Colliery.
Two horizontal twin-cylinder winding engines.
Robey. 1922. Working.
22 in × 3 ft 6 in: 50 rpm: 105 psi.

Mansfield
SK 537 625

Sherwood Colliery.
Horizontal cross compound winding engine.
Fraser & Chalmers. 1903. Working.

Horizontal twin-cylinder winding engine.
Fraser & Chalmers. 1903. Working.

Nottingham

*Industrial Museum, Courtyard Buildings, Wollaton
Park, Nottingham NG8 2AE.*
The material for this collection, concentrating on lace
making, knitting, and other local industries, is still
mainly in store owing to lack of exhibition space.
Among the steam engines acquired by the museum
are a Woolf compound rotative beam by Hawthorn
(1858) and an early Parsons turbine.

Ollerton
SK 662 674

Ollerton Colliery.
Two horizontal twin-cylinder winding engines.
Markham. 1924. Working.

Papplewick
SK 582 522

Papplewick Pumping Station, Notts W.B.
Two single-cylinder rotative beam pumping engines.
J. Watt. 1884. Preserved (Plate 3).
46 in × 7 ft 6 in: 8–10 rpm: 50 psi: 125 hp.

OXFORDSHIRE

Combe
SP 417 151

Sawmill on Blenheim Estate.
Single-cylinder rotative beam engine.
Poss. Piggot. *c.* 1852? Preserved, workable condition.
18 in × 2 ft 8 in: 50 rpm: 40 psi?: *c.* 20 hp.

Henley-on-
Thames
SU 763 827

W. H. Brakspear & Sons.
Vertical single-cylinder engine.
Riley Manufacturing Co. *c.* 1880. Disused.

Hook Norton
SP 347 334

Hook Norton Brewery.
Horizontal single-cylinder engine.
Buxton & Thornley. 1890s. Working.
12 in × 1 ft 8 in: 120 rpm: 100 psi: 20 hp.

SHROPSHIRE

Shrewsbury
SJ 496 121

Coleham Head Sewage Pumping Station.
Two Woolf compound rotative beam pumping engines.
W. R. Renshaw. 1897. Preserved (Plate 7).
13 in × 3 ft 10 in & 21 in × 4 ft 6 in: 10–12 rpm:
75 psi.

Telford

*Ironbridge Gorge Museum Trust, Southside, Church
Hill, Ironbridge, Telford.*
The museum, combining the well-established company collection at Coalbrookdale with the extensive open-air collection at Blist's Hill and other sites in the district, was formally opened in 1973. There are several excellent steam engines on display, including the spectacular cross-coupled twin-beam blowing engine from Lilleshall at the entrance to the Blist's Hill site, and the horizontal single-cylinder colliery winding engine which has been restored to working order in the simulated coal mine.

SOMERSET

Burrow Bridge
ST 357 306

*Aller Moor Pumping Station, Somerset River
Authority.*
Vertical twin-cylinder engine.
Easton, Amos & Anderson. 1869. Preserved.
13½ in × 2 ft: 48–50 rpm: 60 psi: 75 hp.
Diagonal vee twin engine.
Easton, Amos & Sons. 1864. Preserved.
Inverted vertical twin-cylinder engine.
Easton, Amos & Anderson. 1869. Preserved.

Burrow Bridge
ST 345 288

Curry Moor Pumping Station, Somerset River Authority.
Vertical twin-cylinder engine.
Easton, Amos & Sons. 1864. Preserved (Plate 11).
20 in × 2 ft: 48–50 rpm: 80 psi: 150 hp.

Taunton

Somerset County Museum, Taunton Castle.
Several small engines and a Woolf compound beam engine of *c.* 1856 from Pearsall's Silk Mill: 40 rpm: 100 psi: *c.* 50 hp; maker possibly Easton & Amos.

Taunton
ST 232 246

E. & W. C. French Ltd.
Single-cylinder rotative beam engine.
Bury, Curtis & Kennedy. 1840s. Disused.
15 in × 4 ft: 35 rpm.

STAFFORDSHIRE

Bratch
SO 868 937

Wolverhampton Corp. Water Undertaking.
Two inverted vertical triple expansion pumping engines.
Thornewill & Warham. 1896 & 1897. The engines were probably begun by Watt, but completed by T. & W. after the closure of Watts. Disused.

Burton-on-Trent
SK 263 258

Clay Mills Sewage Pumping Station.
Four Woolf compound rotative beam pumping engines.
Gimson & Co. 1885. Disused, A & B to be scrapped, C & D to be preserved.
24 in × 6 ft & 38 in × 8 ft 6 in: 10½ rpm: 80 psi: 150 hp.

Chorley
SK 061 108

Maple Brook Pumping Station, South Staffs Waterworks.
Inverted vertical triple expansion pumping engine.
Galloways. 1913. Preserved.

Cresswell
SJ 974 395

Pumping Station, Staffs Potteries Water Board.
Two inverted vertical triple expansion pumping engines.
Hathorn Davy. 1932. Working.
Horizontal single-cylinder engine.
Green & Son. Working.

Hopwas
SK 172 049

Pumping Station, South Staffs Waterworks.
Two single-cylinder rotative beam pumping engines.
Gimson & Co. 1880. Disused.
24 in × 5 ft: 20 rpm: 35 psi: ?75 hp.

Lichfield
SK 113 084

Sandfields Pumping Station, South Staffs Waterworks.
Cornish beam pumping engine.
J. Davies. 1873. Preserved.
65 in × 9 ft: 100 psi.

Middleport SJ 860 493	*Burgess & Leigh.* Horizontal single-cylinder engine. Wm Boulton, Burslem. 1888. Working.
Middleport SJ 860 495	*Dunn, Bennett & Co.* Horizontal single-cylinder engine. Poss. *c.* 1880. Working. 13 in × 1 ft 10 in: 85 rpm: 100 psi: 40 hp.
Millmeece SJ 830 339	*Staffs Potteries Water Board.* Horizontal tandem compound pumping engine. Hathorn Davey. 1926. Working. Horizontal tandem compound pumping engine. Ashton, Frost. 1914. Working.
Newcastle- under-Lyme SJ 837 482	*Holditch Colliery.* Two horizontal twin-cylinder winding engines. Worsley Mesnes. 1917 & 1918. Working. 30 in × 5 ft: 30 rpm: 150 psi.
Rugeley SK 038 194	*Brindley Bank Pumping Station, South Staffs Waterworks.* Horizontal tandem compound pumping engine. Hathorn Davey. 1907. Preserved.
Stoke-on-Trent: Etruria SJ 873 467	*Etruscan Bone & Stone Works.* Single-cylinder rotative beam engine. Sherratt of Salford, reputedly *c.* 1839, certainly prior to 1858. Disused. 30 in × 5 ft: 22 rpm: 30 psi: 85 hp.
Tunstall SJ 884 533	*Chatterley-Whitfield Colliery.* Horizontal twin-cylinder winder. Worsley Mesnes. 1914. Working. 36 in × 6 ft: 40 rpm: 150 psi.
Tunstall SJ 857 523	*Alfred Meakin.* Two horizontal single-cylinder engines. Tangyes. 1883. One working, one disused.

SUFFOLK

Combs	*Webbs Tannery, Stowmarket.* Grasshopper single-cylinder beam engine. Disused. 11¼ in × 2 ft 9 in.
Lound TG 502 006	*East Anglian Water Co.* Two single-cylinder grasshopper engines. Easton & Amos. *c.* 1855. Preserved (Plate 5). 15 in × 2 ft: 35–40 rpm: 50 psi: 28 hp.
Newmarket TL 620 639	*Southfields Pumping Station.* Inverted vertical triple expansion pumping engine. Hathorn Davey & Co. *c.* 1910. Disused.

Addington
TQ 371 628

Croydon Corp. Water Undertaking.
Two Woolf compound rotative beam pumping engines.
1. Easton & Anderson. 1888. 2. Glenfield. 1893. Both redundant (but preserved).
20 in × 4 ft & 6 ft: 16–20 rpm: 100 psi: 125 hp.
Vertical single-cylinder engine.
?Easton & Anderson. *c.* 1890.
c. 5 in × 8 in.

Waddon
TQ 313 639

Pumping Station, Croydon Corp. Water Undertaking.
Two horizontal cross compound pumping engines.
Worthington Simpson Ltd. 1910 & 1915. Working.
24 in & 42 in × 3 ft: 20 rpm: 120 psi: 120 hp.

Brede
TQ 814 178

Brede Pumping Station, Hastings Waterworks.
Inverted vertical triple expansion engine.
Tangyes. 1904. On stand-by.

Inverted vertical triple expansion engine.
Worthington Simpson. 1939. On stand-by.

Horndean

Gale & Co. Ltd, The Brewery, Horndean.
?Inverted vertical twin-cylinder engine.
?Plenty. ?1900. Idle.
c. 7½ in × 9 in: 80 rpm: 100 psi: *c.* 25 hp.
?Inverted vertical single-cylinder engine.
Belliss & Morcom. Disused.
7 in × 5 in: 470 rpm: 120 psi: 18 hp.

Horsham
TQ 168 307

King & Barnes Brewery.
Horizontal single-cylinder engine.
E. S. Hindley. Installed 2nd-hand *c.* 1900. Working.
9 in × 9 in: 100 rpm: 100 psi: 15 hp.

Horizontal single-cylinder engine.
Hayward Tyler. 1890s or earlier. Preserved in office.
c. 6 in × 6 in: 120 rpm: 60 psi: 6 hp.

Hove
TQ 286 066

Goldstone Pumping Station, Brighton Corp. Water Dept.
Two Woolf compound rotative beam pumping engines.
Easton, Amos & Sons. 1866. Partially dismantled.
Easton, Amos & Anderson. 1875. Preserved.
28 in × 5 ft 4¾ in & 46 in × 8 ft: 16 rpm: 60 psi.

Horizontal single-cylinder engine.
Easton Amos. *c.* 1870. Disused.
9 in × 1 ft 6 in approx.

Lewes
TQ 414 102
Beard & Co., Star Lane Brewery.
Inverted vertical single-cylinder engine.
A. Shaw. 1900. Disused.

Lewes
TQ 419 103
Harvey & Son, Bridge Wharf Brewery.
Horizontal single-cylinder engine.
Pontifex & Wood. 1880. On stand-by.
9 in × 1 ft 6 in: 100 rpm: 90 psi: *c.* 10 hp.

TYNE AND WEAR

Beamish
*North of England Open Air Museum, Beamish
Hall, Stanley, Co. Durham.*
This ambitious museum is rapidly taking shape on
the site specially acquired for it at Beamish Hall.
It aims at re-creating many aspects of life in an early
industrial community, and includes several steam
engines such as that moved from the adjacent
Beamish colliery, which is an interesting example of
the favoured Durham type of vertical single-cylinder
winding engine. It was made by J. & G. Joicey in
1855, with specifications: *c.* 24 in × 5 ft: 40 rpm,
35 psi.

Elemore
NZ 356 456
Elemore Colliery.
Single-cylinder vertical winding engine.
T. Murray? 1826? Disused.
39 in × 6 ft: 30 rpm: 35 psi.

Newcastle upon
Tyne
*Museum of Science & Engineering, Exhibition Park:
Great North Rd, Newcastle upon Tyne, NE2 4PZ.*
The collection includes a Watt-type single-cylinder
beam engine (*c.* 1830), a grasshopper beam engine
(*c.* 1840), and a beam condensing engine from
Glemsford silk mill, Suffolk, made by J. T. Beale
about 1849 (specifications: 19 in × 2 ft: 34 rpm:
25 psi: 45 hp). There are also some marine engines
and *Turbinia* with the first marine steam turbine
designed by Parsons. The Newcastle University
Museum in the Department of Mining Engineering
contains a model of the engine at Hartley Colliery,
the scene of a tragic mining accident.

Ryhope
NZ 404 525
*Ryhope Pumping Station, Sunderland & South
Shields Water Co.*
Two Woolf compound rotative beam pumping en-
gines.
R. & W. Hawthorn. 1868. Preserved, to be made
workable.
27 in × 5 ft 4 in & 45 in × 8 ft: 8–10 rpm: 40 psi:
60 hp.

Washington   *Washington 'F' Colliery.*
NZ 302 575   Horizontal twin-cylinder winding engine.
Grange Iron Co., Durham. 1888. Disused, to be
preserved.
30 in × 4 ft 6 in: 60 rpm: 80 psi.

WARWICKSHIRE

Napton on the   *Napton Brick Works.*
Hill   Horizontal single-cylinder engine.
SP 454 615   J. Wilkes. *c.* 1880. Disused.

WILTSHIRE

Crofton   *Pumping Station, Kennet and Avon Canal.*
SU 262 623   Two Cornish beam pumping engines.
1. Boulton & Watt. 1812. Converted to Cornish cycle
by Harvey & Co. 1845. Preserved and working.
42 in × 8 ft: 11½ spm: 20 psi: 38–40 hp.

2. James Sims's combined cylinder engine.
Harvey & Co. 1846. Reconstructed with single
cylinder by Wm Rollinson & Sons, 1903. Preserved
and working.
42 in × 8 ft: 11½ spm: 20 psi: 38–40 hp.

Devizes   *Wadworth & Co. Ltd.*
SU 002 616   Horizontal single-cylinder engine.
Adlam & Co. *c.* 1885. Disused, possibly workable.
10 in × 1 ft 6 in: 100 rpm: 100 psi: 25 hp.

YORKSHIRE (North Yorkshire)

Bradley   *P. Green & Co.*
SE 002 484   Horizontal tandem compound engine.
Smith Bros. & Eastwood. 1901. Working.
14 in & 28 in × 3 ft 6 in: 80 rpm: 140 psi: 300 hp.

Brayton Barff   *Pumping Station, Pontefract, Goole and Selby Water*
SE 587 301   *Board.*
Inverted vertical triple expansion pumping engine.
J. Watt & Co. 1906. Preserved.
13 in–20 in–34 in × 2 ft: 27 rpm: 150 psi: 70 hp.

High Bentham   *Wenning Silks Ltd.*
SD 665 687?   Horizontal tandem compound engine.
Pollit & Wigzell. 1926. Disused.

Roall   *Pumping Station, Pontefract, Goole and Selby Water*
SE 568 244   *Board.*
Woolf compound rotative beam pumping engine.
Easton & Anderson. 1891. Preserved (Plate 4).
14 in × 3 ft & 20 in × 4 ft: 20 rpm: 120 psi.

York

National Railway Museum.
In addition to locomotives and rolling stock, this new museum contains two distinguished stationary engines:
Stanhope & Tyne Railway winding engine from Weatherhill.
Vertical, with large flywheel, 1833.
29 in × 5 ft: 60 psi.
Leicester & Swannington Railway winding engine from Swannington Incline.
Horizontal, with piston valves, slide for tail rod, and lattice eccentrics.
Horsley Iron & Coal Co. designed by R. Stephenson, 1833.
Claimed to be the oldest surviving horizontal engine.
18¼ in × 3 ft 6 in: 80 psi.

YORKSHIRE (South Yorkshire)

Aldwick Le
Street
SE 540 097

Bullcroft Colliery.
Two horizontal twin-cylinder winding engines.
Markham & Co. 1910. Derelict.
30 in × 6 ft: 180 psi: 1,800 hp.

Armthorpe
SE 617 046

Markham Main Colliery.
Two horizontal twin-cylinder winding engines.
Markham & Co. 1920. Working.

Askern
SE 558 138

Askern Main Colliery.
Two horizontal twin tandem winding engines.
Yates & Thom. 1911. Working
36 in & 60 in × 6 ft: 35 rpm: 160 psi.

Barkisland
SE 055 183

E. Sykes & Sons.
Horizontal tandem compound engine.
Pollit & Wigzell. 1899. Working.

Bentley
SE 570 075

Bentley Colliery.
Two horizontal cross compound winding engines.
Fraser & Chalmers. 1908. Working.
c. 35 in & 56 in × 6 ft: 40 rpm: 160 psi.

Dinnington
SK 518 867

Dinnington Colliery.
Two horizontal twin-cylinder winding engines.
Markham & Co. 1911. Working.
34 in × 6 ft: 150 psi; and 40 in × 6 ft 6 in: 150 psi.

Doncaster

Cusworth Hall Industrial Museum, Cusworth Hall.
There are several small steam engines in this collection.

Edlington
SK 544 992

Yorkshire Main Colliery.
Two horizontal twin-cylinder winding engines.
Markham & Co. 1909. Working.

Elsecar SE 387 000	*Elsecar Colliery.* Newcomen engine. 1795. Preserved. 48 in × *c.* 5 ft: 6 spm.
Hatfield/ Stainforth SE 653 113	*Hatfield Colliery.* Horizontal twin-cylinder winding engine. J. Musgrave. 1921. Working. 42 in × 7 ft: 40 rpm: 160 psi.
Hickleton SE 465 053	*Hickleton Colliery.* Horizontal twin-cylinder winding engine. Markham & Co. 1921. Working.
Little Houghton SE 420 060	*Houghton Main Colliery.* Horizontal twin-cylinder winding engine. Bradley & Craven. 1938. Working.
Pickburn SE 526 077	*Brodsworth Main Colliery.* Horizontal twin-cylinder winding engine. Markham & Co. 1923 or 1924. Working.
Sheffield SK 325 820	*Abbeydale Works, Sheffield City Museums.* Horizontal single-cylinder engine. *c.* 1850. Preserved.
Sheffield	*English Steel Corporation, River Don works.* Three-cylinder simple vertical (rolling mill) engine. Davy Bros. 1905. Works occasionally. 40 in × 4 ft 6 in: 120 rpm: 160 psi: 12,000 hp.
Sheffield SK 295 898	*T. Wragg & Sons.* Horizontal single-cylinder engine. Thornewill & Warham. 1924. Disused. 20 in × 3 ft: 80 rpm: 120 psi: 200 hp
Thurcroft SK 499 897	*Thurcroft Colliery.* Horizontal twin-cylinder winding engine. Markham & Co. 1911. Working. Horizontal cross compound (compressor) engine. Walker Bros. *c.* 1926. On stand-by.

YORKSHIRE (West Yorkshire)

Bradford	*Bradford Industrial Museum, Moorside Mills, Eccleshill, Bradford, BD2 3HP.* Appropriately housed in a disused textile mill, this collection includes among several interesting steam engines a single McNaught beam engine (Bracewell, 1865: 18 in × 2 ft and 24 in × 4 ft: 52 rpm: 85 psi: 160 hp) and two horizontal single-cylinder engines (Carr & Foster, *c.* 1900; and Clabour, 1906, respectively). (See also Plate 21.)

Bradford
SE 193 340

J. C. Crabtree.
Inverted vertical compound engine.
Cole, Marchent & Morley. 1907. Disused.
20 in & 36 in × 3 ft: 110 rpm: 150 psi: 700 hp.

Bradford
SE 172 333

Holmes, Mann & Co.
Horizontal cross compound engine.
Newton, Bean & Mitchell. 1921. Working.
20 in & 40 in × 2 ft 6 in: 100 rpm: 120 psi: 650 hp.

Single-cylinder horizontal engine.
Newton, Bean & Mitchell. 1892. Installed, 2nd-hand,
1921. Working.
17 in × 2 ft 6 in: 100 rpm: 120 psi: 100 hp.

Bradford
SE 108 320

J. Whitehead & Sons.
Horizontal single-cylinder engine.
T. Bradford. Disused.
12 in × 2 ft 2 in: 120 rpm; 75 psi.

Bradford
SE 189 328

W. & J. Whitehead Ltd.
Tandem extraction engine.
Sulzer Bros. 1919. On stand-by.
24⅝ in & 37½ in × 2 ft 11½ in: 133 rpm: 180 psi:
1,500 hp.

Bramley
SE 247 345

Winerite Ltd.
Horizontal tandem compound engine.
Cole, Marchent & Morley. 1914. Preserved for the
time being.
15½ & 30 in × 3 ft 6 in: 96 rpm: 160 psi: 450 hp.

Castleford
SE 436 241

Glass Houghton Colliery.
Horizontal cross compound (fan) engine.
Walker Bros. 1918. On stand-by.
26 in & 39 in × 3 ft 6 in: 60 rpm: 140 psi: *c.* 600 hp.

Denby Dale
SE 228 083

J. Kenyon & Sons.
Vertical cross compound engine.
Maker and date uncertain. Rebuilt by Lumb. *c.* 1900.
Working.
14 in × 26 in × 3 ft: 60 rpm: 85 psi: 150 hp.

Dewsbury
SE 257 213

Wm Greenwood & Son Ltd, Providence Mill.
Horizontal tandem compound.
Wood & Baldwin? 1885. Disused.
15 in & 24 in × 3 ft: 85 rpm: 120 psi: 250 hp.

Elland
SE 118 225

W. T. Knowles & Sons.
Horizontal tandem compound.
Hick, Hargreaves & Co. 1883. Working.
15 in & 30 in × 4 ft: 80 rpm: 160 psi: 350 hp.

Elland
SE 067 200

J. Maude & Sons.
Horizontal cross compound engine.

Pollit & Wigzell. 1920. Working.
18 in & 36 in × 3 ft 6 in: 80 rpm: 150 psi: 450 hp.

Holmfirth
SE 120 068

W. H. & J. Barber.
Uniflow engine.
Clayton & Goodfellows. 1922. Working.
24 in × 2 ft 6 in: 150 rpm: 150 psi: 520 hp.

Holmfirth
SE 164 074

Dobroyd Ltd.
Uniflow engine.
Woodhouse & Mitchell. 1920. Disused.
24 in × 2 ft 6 in: 140 rpm: 160 psi: 400 hp.
Uniflow engine.
Pollit & Wigzell. 1924. Disused.
24 in × 2 ft 6 in: 132 rpm: 160 psi: 500 hp.

Holmfirth
SE 143 067

J. Watkinson & Sons.
Horizontal tandem compound engine.
Pollit & Wigzell Ltd. 1909. Working.
18 in & 34 in & 4 ft: 80 rpm: 160 psi: 600 hp.

Honley
SE 135 123

T. Lees & Co.
Horizontal single-cylinder engine.
J. Kilburn. 1872. Working, due to be scrapped.
20 in × 3 ft: 70 rpm: 55 psi: c. 80 hp.

Huddersfield
SE 111 164

Job Beaumont & Sons Ltd.
Horizontal tandem compound engine.
J. & E. Wood. 1903. Working.
16 in & 29 in × 4 ft: 67 rpm: 140 psi: 500 hp.

Huddersfield
SE 111 158

Colne Vale Dye & Chemical Co.
Horizontal single-cylinder engine.
Working.
$13\frac{1}{2}$ in × 2 ft: 100 rpm: 100 psi: 60 hp.

Huddersfield
SE 149 168

Jarratt, Pyrah & Armitage.
Horizontal tandem compound engine, originally 1884.
Compounded by J. Wood. c. 1906. Working.
11 in & $18\frac{1}{2}$ in × 3 ft: 104 rpm: 100 psi: 150 hp.

Huddersfield

Tolson Memorial Museum, Ravensknowle Park, Huddersfield.
Contains a horizontal single-cylinder engine with return connecting rod, dating from the 1850s. (9 in × 2 ft: 40 rpm: 50 psi: c. 20 hp.) (Plate 17.)

Leeds

Leeds City Museums, Municipal Buildings, Leeds 1.
A project for an industrial museum in Leeds is now taking shape in a disused textile mill converted for the purpose.

Leeds

W. & H. Miers Ltd, Embro Works, Dewsbury Rd, Leeds 11.

Horizontal single-cylinder engine.
Newton, Bean & Mitchell.

Leeds

E. J. Rawlins & Co. Ltd, Burley Rd.
Inverted vertical single-cylinder engine.
Marshall.
9 in × 1 ft: 160 rpm max.: 100 psi: 25 hp.

Leeds
SE 194 332

United Leeds Hospitals Central Laundry.
Horizontal tandem compound engine.
Hick, Hargreaves & Co. 1896. Working.

Mirfield
SE 202 195

G. Lyles & Sons.
Pusher compounded single-cylinder rotative beam
engine.
Pusher: Horizontal single-cylinder engine, maker
unknown, installed 1900. Cylinder by Marsdens;
new valve gear by Newton, Bean & Mitchell, 1906.
Preserved.
Beam 35¼ in × 6 ft
Pusher 19 in × 6 ft } 42 rpm: 160 psi: *c.* 400 hp.

Ossett
SE 270 202

J. M. Briggs' Runtlings Mill.
Horizontal tandem compound engine.
Marsden's Engines. 1908. Working.
12 in & 23 in × 3 ft 6 in: 82 rpm: 120 psi: 250 hp.

Otley
SE 207 456

W. Barker & Son, Tannery.
Horizontal single-cylinder engine.
Marsden's Engines. 1907. Working.
c. 16 in × 2 ft.

Overton
SE 253 165

Caphouse Colliery.
Horizontal twin-cylinder winding engine.
Davy Bros. 1876. Worked occasionally.
16 in × 3 ft: 80 psi.

Pudsey
SE 226 322

J. G. Mohun & Son.
Horizontal single-cylinder engine.
Newton Bean & Mitchell. 1926. Working.
16½ in × 2 ft: 120 rpm: 160 psi: *c.* 120 hp.

Scissett
SE 247 101

G. H. Norton & Co.
Horizontal tandem compound engine.
Pollit & Wigzell. 1886.
13 in & 26 in × 6 ft: 55 rpm: 100 psi: 350 hp.

Shepley
SE 200 107

Firth Bros.
Inverted vertical triple expansion engine.
Wood Bros. *c.* 1900. Works occasionally.
15 in–22 in–34 in × 3 ft 6 in: 85 rpm: 150 psi: 600
hp.

Shipley
SE 147 377

G. R. Morrison Ltd.
Horizontal tandem compound engine. *c.* 1880.

Compounded by J. & W. McNaught? *c.* 1910. Working.
12 in & 24 in × 3 ft approx.: 96 rpm: 100 psi: 120 hp.

Silsden
SE 044 462
Taylor Bros.
Inverted vertical cross compound engine.
Scott & Hodgson. 1896. Working.
17 in & 35 in × 4 ft: 75 rpm: 160 psi: 700 hp.

Slaithwaite
SE 068 144
J. Beaumont Jnr Ltd.
Compound vertical grasshopper engine.
Schofield & Taylor. 1887. Disused.
11 in × 3 ft 6 in & 22 in × 3 ft: 60 rpm: 130 psi: 200 hp.

Slaithwaite
SE 076 138
Elon Crowther & Sons.
Horizontal tandem compound engine.
Pollit & Wigzell. 1910. On stand-by.
14 in & 28 in × 2 ft 9 in: 83 rpm: 150 psi: 250 hp.

Inverted vertical compound engine (enclosed).
Belliss & Morcom. 1953. On stand-by.
220 hp coupled to Brush alternator.

Stainland
J. Maude & Sons (Stainland Ltd), Bankhouse Mills, Elland.
Horizontal cross compound engine.
Pollit & Wigzell. 1920. Working.
18 in & 36 in × 3 ft 6 in: 80 rpm: 150 psi: 450 hp.

Todmorden
SD 952 245
Nelson's Milstead Mill.
Horizontal tandem compound engine.
Poss. Wood Bros. 1874. Poss. compounded by Ebor Engineering Co. Disused.
14 in & 28 in × 3 ft 6 in: 62 rpm: 120 psi: *c.* 300 hp.

Wakefield
SE 309 214
Matthew Walker & Sons.
Horizontal cross compound engine.
Pollit & Wigzell. 1912. Disused, workable.
19 in & 37 in × 4 ft: 84 rpm: 150 psi: 750 hp.

Walton
SE 360 182
Walton Colliery.
Horizontal twin-cylinder winding engine.
Robey & Co. 1923. Working.
34 in × 5 ft.

Horizontal twin-cylinder winding engine.
J. Fowler & Co. 1894. Working.
?42 in × 7 ft: ?80 psi.

Yeadon
SE 205 412
J. Ives & Co., Manor Mill.
Horizontal tandem compound engine.
Pollit & Wigzell. 1920. Working.
15 in & 33 in × 4 ft: 75 rpm: 120 psi: 400 hp.

WALES

CLWYD (Flintshire etc.)

Rhydymwyn
SJ 205 675

Hartley & Partners.
Horizontal cross compound engine.
Robey & Co. 1903. Disused.

DYFED (Carmarthenshire etc.)

Kidwelly
SN 422 079

Kidwelly Tinplate Works.
Horizontal tandem compound engine.
Cole Marchent & Morley. c. 1920. Disused.
500 hp.

Two inverted vertical tandem compound engines.
Foden. c. 1880, probably compounded later. Disused.
24 in & 48 in × 4 ft: 30 rpm: 120 psi: c. 400 hp.

Llangennach
SN 573 023

Morlais Colliery.
Horizontal twin-cylinder winding engine.
A. Barclay & Co. 1907. Working.
20 in × 2 ft: 60 rpm: 90 psi.

Horizontal cross compound winding engine.
A. Barclay. Working.
15 in & 24 in & 2 ft 6 in: 120 rpm: 90 psi.

GLAMORGAN (Mid-Glamorgan)

Mountain Ash
ST 050 990

Abergorki Colliery or Deep Navigation Colliery.
Waddle fan engine.
Waddle Patent Fan & Engineering Co. 1870? Preserved.
20 in × 3 ft: 50 rpm: 80 psi: 120 hp.

Single-cylinder horizontal capstan engine.
Nevill. c. 1870. Disused.
16 in × 3 ft.

New Tredegar
c. SO 147 027

Elliott Colliery.
Horizontal twin tandem compound winding engine.
Thornewill & Warham. 1891. Preserved.
28 in & 42 in × 6 ft: 20 rpm: 160 psi.

Pontypridd
ST 054 910

Tymawr Colliery.
Horizontal twin-cylinder winding engine.
Barker & Cope. 1875. Working on compressed air.
36 in × 6 ft: 45 rpm: 80 psi.

Trehafod
ST 039 911

Lewis Merthyr Colliery.
Horizontal twin-cylinder winding engine.
Worsley Mesnes Ironworks Co. 1890. Working on
compressed air.
34 in × 5 ft.

Horizontal twin-cylinder winding engine.
J. D. Leigh. 1893. Derelict.
26 in × 4 ft.

GLAMORGAN (South-Glamorgan)

Cardiff
National Museum of Wales, Cardiff CF1 3NP.
The Department of Industry and Technology covers
the major industries of South Wales, with a particularly good collection on coal mining. There are
several steam engines here, including one preserved
as an external feature in the grounds of the Museum.

Llanishen
ST 190 820
Llanishen Water Works.
Single-cylinder beam pumping engine.
Harvey. 1850s. Preserved.
20 in × 3 ft 6 in.

GLAMORGAN (West-Glamorgan)

Crynant
SN 785 032
Blaenant Colliery.
Horizontal twin-cylinder winding engine.
Markham & Co. 1907. Disused.
32 in × 5 ft: 50 rpm: 160 psi.

Horizontal twin-cylinder winding engine.
Worsley Mesnes Ironworks Ltd. 1927. Working.

Horizontal twin-cylinder capstan engine.
Qualter Hall, Barnsley. 1925. Disused.
9 in × 1 ft: 100 rpm: 120 psi: 25 hp.

Horizontal single-cylinder capstan engine.
Llewellyn & Cubitt. Disused.

GWENT (Monmouthshire etc.)

Abersychan
SO 244 020
Blaenserchan Colliery.
Horizontal twin-cylinder capstan engine.
Maker unknown.

Crumlin
ST 212 988
Crumlin Navigation Colliery
Horizontal twin tandem triple expansion fan engine.
Walker Bros. Preserved.
15 in–23½ in & 2 × 26 in × 3 ft 3 in: 60 rpm: 160
psi: *c.* 500 hp.

Pontypool
ST 265 999
Glyn Pits.
Single-cylinder rotative beam pumping engine
(double-acting).
Neath Abbey Engineering Works. 1845. Derelict.
30 in × 6 ft: 18–20 rpm: 50–60 psi.

Single-cylinder vertical winding engine.
Neath Abbey Works. 1840–45. Derelict.
36 in × 5 ft: 30 rpm: 60 psi.

Tirpentwys ST 247 999	*Tirpentwys Colliery.* Horizontal twin-cylinder haulage engine. Daglish. Underground. To be removed to National Museum of Wales.
Treforest ST 081 885	*Treforest Mining School.* Single-cylinder rotative beam winding engine. J. Calvert. 1844? Preserved.

GWYNEDD (Caernarvonshire etc.)

Llanberis SH 593 598	*Dinorwic Slate Quarry.* Three? horizontal cross compound engines. Ingersol Rand Co. Preserved.
Nantlle SH 498 531 approx.	*Dorothea Slate Quarries.* Cornish beam pumping engine. Holman Bros. 1904. Des. Nicholas Trestrail. Preserved to be made workable. 68 in × 10 ft: 6½ spm: 40 psi. Vertical single-cylinder engine. Mather? 1850s. Preserved. 18 in × 3 ft: 60 rpm: 25 hp.

SCOTLAND

ABERDEENSHIRE

Aberdeen	*Aberdeen Docks, Fishbox Sawmills.* Horizontal single-cylinder engine. Working.
Garlogie NJ 783 055	*Dunecht Estate, Skene Parish.* Beam (rotative) engine. Pre-1837. Derelict and partly dismantled.

ANGUS

Dundee	*Seabrae Sawmill* Horizontal side-by-side compound engine. Maker unknown.

AYRSHIRE

Auchinleck NS 549 216	*Highhouse Colliery.* Horizontal twin-cylinder winding engine. Grant, Ritchie & Co. 1896. Working. 20 in × 4 ft: 36 rpm: 70–80 psi.

CLACKMANNANSHIRE

Alloa	*Glentana Mills Ltd, Dalmore Works.* Horizontal single-cylinder engine.

G

Douglas & Grant. 1923. Working.
12 in × 2 ft 6 in: 90 rpm: 100 psi: 80 hp.

DUNBARTONSHIRE

Dumbarton
NS 397 753

(*Now in Dumbarton Town Centre*).
Marine side-lever engine by Napier.
1824 (Plate 12).
30 in × 3 ft 6 in: 2–4 psi.

FIFE

Leslie

Smith, Anderson & Co., Fettykil Mills.
Inverted vertical single-cylinder engine.
J. Milne & Co. 1897. Preserved.

Leven

J. Donaldson & Co. Wemyss Sawmills.
Horizontal tandem compound engine.
J. Carmichael & Co. 1923. Working.
18 in & 30 in × 3 ft: 80 rpm: 120 psi: 350 hp.

LANARKSHIRE

Cadder
NS 666 683

Cardowan Colliery.
Two horizontal twin-cylinder winding engines.
Murray & Patterson. 1924. At least one working.
26 in × 5 ft: 36 rpm: 120 psi.

Glasgow

*Wm Beardmore & Co., Parkhead Steelworks, Glasgow
31.*
Twin-cylinder horizontal rolling-mill engine.
D. Stewart. 1942. Working.
42 in × 5 ft: 120 rpm: 120 psi: 3,000 hp.

Glasgow

Art Gallery & Museum, Kelvingrove, Glasgow C3.
The Kelvingrove collection contains some interesting
steam engines, mainly concerned with marine services, including a quarter-size model of the Steeple
engine built in 1854 by Todd & McGregor of Partick
for the ss *Simla*. There is also on display a side-lever
engine (1821: *c.* 18 in × 3 ft) and the cylinder of
the *Comet* steam ship of 1812 (*c.* 15 in × 2 ft 6 in),
and there are other engines in store.

Glasgow

Museum of Transport, 25 Albert Drive, Glasgow 5.
This museum is concerned mainly with road and rail
transport, but it contains several steam-engine
items including some which are kept in store for the
Kelvingrove collection.

Greenock

*The McLean Museum & Greenock Art Gallery, 9
Union St, Greenock, Renfrewshire.*
Contains a number of steam-engine models.

Newmains	*Kingshill Colliery.* Two horizontal twin-cylinder winding engines. A. Barclay, 1924, and Shearer & Pettigrew, 1880s. Both probably working. Barclay : 28 in × 5 ft: 110 rpm max.: 110 psi. S. & P.: 24 in × 4 ft 6 in: 25 rpm: 110 psi.
Strathaven	*Elder & Watson Ltd, Hosiery Works, Dunlop St.* Horizontal single-cylinder engine. ?Crowhall & Campbell. c. 1850.

EAST LOTHIAN

Prestonpans NT 374 737	*Prestongrange Colliery.* Cornish beam pumping engine. Harvey & Co. 1874. Preserved. 70 in × 12 ft.

MIDLOTHIAN

Edinburgh	*Royal Scottish Museum, Chambers St, Edinburgh EH1 1JF.* There is an excellent collection of engines in this museum, covering the main phases in the evolution of steam technology from the Newcomen atmospheric (the metal parts of a machine built at Carron c. 1770), through Boulton & Watt to horizontal arrangements and high-speed generators manufactured in the present century.
Newton Grange NT 333 639	*Lady Victoria Colliery.* Horizontal twin-cylinder winding engine. Grant, Ritchie & Co. c. 1894. Working. 42 in × 7 ft: 60 rpm max.: 100 psi: ?1,600 hp.

PERTHSHIRE

Auchterarder	*R. White & Co., Glenruthven Mills.* Horizontal tandem compound engine. 1873. Working. 10½ in & 20 in × 2 ft 6 in: 62 rpm: 60 psi: ?100 hp.
Blairgowrie	*T. Thompson (Blairgowrie) Ltd, Ashgrove Works.* Horizontal single-cylinder engine. Pierce Bros. 1865. Disused. 24 in × 3 ft.
Blairgowrie	*T. Thompson (Blairgowrie) Ltd, Keathbank Works.* Horizontal single-cylinder engine. 1864–5. Disused. Future doubtful. 21 in × 4 ft: 30 rpm: 75 psi: ?70 hp.
Dunblane	*Wilson's (Dunblane) Ltd, Springbank Mills.* Horizontal cross compound engine.

Robey & Co. Ltd. 1927. Disused.
10 in & 14 in × 2 ft 6 in: 120 rpm: 180 psi: 170 hp.

RENFREWSHIRE

Paisley

Seedhill Finishing Co., Ralston St.
Two inverted vertical twin-cylinder engines (enclosed).
J. Howden & Co. Generator. On stand-by.

Renfrew
NS 510 683

Grasshopper side-lever beam engine.
Inglis. 1851. Preserved in open air at Renfrew Ferry (Plate 13).
33 in × 4 ft 8 in.

SELKIRK

Selkirk

Law Textiles (Selkirk) Ltd, Forest Mill.
Horizontal twin tandem compound engine.
J. Petrie & Co. 1911. On stand-by.
12 in & 24 in × 2 ft 6 in: 100 rpm: 75 psi: 450 hp.

STIRLINGSHIRE

Stirling
NS 837 914

Polmaise Colliery.
Horizontal twin-cylinder winding engine.
Grant, Ritchie & Co. 1903. Existence doubtful.
26 in × 5 ft: 50 rpm: 100 psi.

SUTHERLAND

Brora
NC 900 040

Brora Colliery.
Horizontal twin-cylinder winding engine.
J. Wood, Wigan. Present status uncertain.
c. 9 in × 2 ft.

Captions to Plates

Plate 1. Kew Bridge Pumping Station(Metropolitan Water Board)

The Cornish engine was impressive for its size and stately motion, and this is a fine example of the type at its best. Made by the Copperhouse Foundry, Hayle, in 1845, it is a 90 in (the Cornish engine was sized by the cylinder bore in inches) with 11 ft stroke, and developed 400 hp when running at 8 strokes per minute, with steam at 40 psi. The pump is a single-acting plunger 46 in in diameter (seen at the left of the plate) and pumped 5,000,000 gallons per day against a head of 182 ft. It was still in use for 96 per cent of the time in 1913, and Kew was a remarkable station in which all of the engines were of the Cornish type, without flywheels or crankshafts. The engines are outstanding examples of the fine work of the county when Harveys of Hayle maintained a branch in London with fitters, carpenters and painters, and engine drivers also, at the time when they were also responsible for the running of the engines. A standpipe was fitted outside the station to maintain a full head on the engines if a water main burst. The photograph was taken when the engines were in full use, and shows the high standards which, provided by the Cornish engineers, were fully maintained by the Water Board. The station is now in the care of the Kew Bridge Trust.

Plate 2. Springhead Pumping Station (Hull Waterworks)

This is a fine example of North Country engineering and enlightened civic approach which pumped from a well to the reservoirs, against a total head which varied from 130 to 200 ft. It was made by Bells, Lightfoot & Co., Newcastle-upon-Tyne, in 1876, the steam cylinder being 90 in. The two well pumps 27 in, and the single surface lift pump 36 in in diameter, all by 11 ft stroke, pumped 7,500,000 gallons per day maximum. The beam is of the box type, built up from wrought-iron plates and angles, and the finish everywhere is of a high order. The outstanding feature of the engine however is that although of the Cornish type which was best adopted to a constant head, this one worked against a variable head of 130 to 200 ft, and since in the Cornish cycle the pumping was done by the weight of the pump rods or the balance box, it was necessary here to vary the loading with the head. This was provided for by making the balance box as a massive fluted cast-iron water tank some 7 ft in diameter, seen within the railings nearer to the camera. Water could be added to this by the pipe seen

descending from the upper floor into the box when extra loading was
necessary for the higher head, and a drain valve was fitted below the
tank by which water could be drained off, when the loading had to be
reduced, as when pumping to a lower head. It was an ingenious solution
to a problem rarely met with a Cornish waterworks engine.

Plate 3. Papplewick Pumping Station (Nottingham Waterworks)

Plates 1 and 2 were of engines in which the movements were regulated
entirely by the setting of the steam valves, but most waterworks
engines were rotative and provided with a crank and connecting-rod
system to regulate the motion as in this example. Papplewick station
followed those at Basford (1857) and Bestwood (1873), and started
working in 1884. The two engines were made by James Watt & Co.,
each with a single cylinder 46 in bore × 7 ft 6 in stroke, fitted with
drop valves. The well pumps were driven from the beam at the flywheel
end, by rods passing either side of the crank, and the water was pumped
to the reservoirs by a pump placed between the cylinder and the
supporting columns, each engine pumping 1,500,000 gallons per day
against a head of 250 ft. The engine is seen in working condition about
1936, and the finish and maintenance were very fine. The stained glass
in the engine-room windows is most attractive, as is the filigree decorative work upon the columns supporting the sway beam centres, the
columns being capped by highly ornate capitals. One engine was run at a
time, and happily the two engines were retained together with the
engine and boiler houses and chimney complex, a fine example of the
best late-Victorian engineering practice. Each of the engines developed
125 hp at 8–10 rpm, using steam at 50 psi.

Plate 4. Roall Pumping Station (The Pontefract, Goole and Selby
Water Board)

This Water Board was supplied by three steam pumping stations, at
Roall, Brayton and Eggborough. The authorities preserved an engine
at Roall and at Brayton, but Eggborough (1933) has disappeared. The
Roall engine seen in the plate is a typical medium-sized plain but neat
and practical design of the late nineteenth century. Made by Easton &
Anderson of London and Erith, it is a Woolf compound with cylinders of
about 14 in and 20 in bore, by 3 ft and 4 ft strokes, fitted with plain
slide valves. Originally there were two engines placed end to end in the
house, but one was removed for the installation of diesel pumps.
Everything about the engines that could be was made of cast iron, and
throughout the design is very neat although plain. The foundry work is
of the highest order. As seen in the early 1960s it was very well kept,
and represents the late phase of an old-established concern whose
designs became progressively more plain and practical. The absence of
the once essential blacksmith's work is notable: even the usual forged
looped links of the parallel motion are absent, superseded by a plain
turned design.

Plate 5. Lound Pumping Station (Lowestoft Water Works)

The plant is compact, and probably dates from about 1855. It was made by Easton & Amos, London. The engines are of the grasshopper type, in which the beam is suspended from one end upon a swinging link, with the cylinder at the other end, and with the connecting rod near to the cylinder. They developed about 28 hp, at 35–40 rpm, using steam at about 50 psi, and they are probably the last Easton engines to survive with the highly attractive curved brackets for the parallel-motion rods. Other interesting features are the neat shape of the vertical swinging link supporting the end of the beam, and the early type of eye bolts for the piston and valve rod glands. The installation of two engines in line with each other was unusual, as most of the grasshopper installations were of a single engine only. It was a fairly fast engine driving the pumps through gearing, which with mortise (wooden) teeth was very quiet. The demand for water outstripped the capacity of these delightful little engines possibly in the 1920s, but happily they have survived as an example of high-class waterworks practice of the mid-nineteenth century.

Plate 6. Crossness Pumping Station (London Main Drainage System)

The importance of town main drainage and sewage removal was recognized in the mid-nineteenth century, and one of the earliest and certainly the largest scheme was that for London, where the low-lying area along the riverside had long been unhealthy. It required four pumping stations, containing twenty beam engines all with single cylinders, and twelve of these engines were later converted to compound steam cycles with new cylinders and boilers. The four engines at Crossness were built by James Watt & Co. in 1865, with cylinders 48 in bore × 9 ft stroke, and they were converted to triple-expansion working by Benjamin Goodfellows of Hyde in 1891, who fitted new Corliss valve cylinders of 19 in, 32 in and 44 in bore, which together with new boilers cost £21,916; these are the cylinders there now. Various other engines were added as the load grew, but the beam engines are otherwise unaltered. The decorative works seen around the centre of the engine room and the railings are very fine, and the engines with their great sway beams some 40 ft long, overhead, are a fine example of the grandeur of Victorian engineering. An interesting feature is that although the connecting rods are forged wrought iron, the splendid cruciform section pump rods are of cast iron. Permission to view can be obtained from the Greater London Council.

Plate 7. Coleham Sewage Pumping Station (Shrewsbury)

Shrewsbury depends upon pumping to avoid flooding, a duty performed for over seventy years by a pair of beam engines until electrically-driven plant was installed. The engines are a pair of Woolf compounds with slide valve high-pressure cylinders 13 in × 3 ft 10 in, and drop valve low-pressures 21 in bore × 4 ft 6 in stroke, and with a pump on either side of the beam centres. The design is very practical, as the cylinders, columns, and crankshaft bearings are all mounted upon a deep bedplate allowing most of the fitting to be done in the workshop, needing little on the site. The use of slide valves on the high-, and drop valves on the low-pressure cylinders, is the reverse to usual practice, and another interesting feature is that the riding cut-off valve on the high-pressure cylinder is driven from the beam itself, whereas a separate eccentric was usually fitted. They used steam at 75 psi, from Cornish boilers, and usually ran at 10–12 rpm to pump up to 2,000,000 gallons per day to a 35 ft head. They have happily been retained upon the site, and are open to visitors on Wednesday and Friday afternoons from 14.00 to 17.00 hours. One is turned slowly by an electric motor, when the action of the high-pressure valve can be seen through clear panels on the chest.

Plate 8. Abbey Lane Sewage Pumping Station (City of Leicester)

Leicester depends upon pumping to prevent flooding, and adopted Woolf compound beam engines for the service. The scheme was on a grand scale, with the unusual feature of four large beam engines in a row in one engine room. The cylinders are 30 in bore × 5 ft 9 in stroke for the high-, and 48 in × 8 ft 6 in for the low-pressure cylinders, each cylinder being fitted with a piston valve, with an internal cut-off valve working inside the main valves. The four eccentrics for operating the piston valves of each engine are placed upon a side shaft, which is driven by bevel teeth upon the face of the flywheel, from which the governors are also driven. There are two pumps to each engine, one driven directly from the beam, and the other from a tail rod below the high-pressure piston. They are in process of restoration for exhibition. The neat timber lagging upon the cylinders and valve chests, the tiling of the engine room, and the decorative moulding upon the columns are good examples of the work that local craftsmen could achieve, when backed by an enlightened patron.

Plate 9. Cheddars Lane Sewage Pumping Station (City of Cambridge)

The two Davey differential steam pumps are probably the last remaining civic examples of a non-rotative design which was once widely used in town and mining service. They were very well maintained, and other plant was added as the load grew, and finally a new station led to the closure of Cheddars Lane. The engines are a pair of horizontal compound differential engines made by Hathorn Davey & Co. of Sun Foundry, Leeds, in 1894, works No. 5148, and are interesting in that the steam piston rods are coupled to twin discs, from which the pumps are also driven by pins between them. There is a pump on either side of the centre of the disc, and the phasing allows expansive working. The steam cylinders are 22 in and 44 in bores × 4 ft stroke, and they were designed to pump 577 gallons per minute through three miles of mains to the treatment plant against a head of 40 ft. The steam cylinders are fitted with slide valves driven through a differential motion, and, using steam at 100 psi, they ran at 14 double strokes per minute. The high-pressure cylinder and pump gear are carried upon a deep girder on each side, with the low-pressure cylinder mounted upon its own short bed. The engines are now in the care of the Cambridge Museum of Technology Trust, and are being restored.

Plate 10. Stretham Pumping Station (The Waterbeach Drainage Level, Ely)

Drainage of the area of 5,600 acres was started in 1831 by a scoop-type water-lifting wheel driven by a beam engine made by the Butterley Co., and this plant has been preserved. The steam cylinder is 39 in bore × 8 ft stroke, which with steam at 5 psi developed 70–80 hp at 17 rpm. The pressure was later raised to 10 psi, and Petries of Rochdale fitted piston valves and chests, which, with improvements in the scoop wheel, gave reduced fuel consumption. The engine was otherwise unaltered in nearly a century of service, but, as usual with land drainage, the ground level sank. The scoop wheel had to be increased in diameter, firstly to 33 ft 6 in in 1850, and then to 37 ft 6 in in 1896, the paddles or ladles being reduced in width each time, to compensate for the increased diameter. The maximum power, 105 hp, was developed when, once, the water had to be lifted 9 ft. It was the only drainage unit for the level until in 1925 the boilers were unsound for the second time in its long life, and a diesel engine was installed; the steam plant was then standby until it was run for the last time in 1941. Stretham is the only pumping station in which the three stages of the development exist together, since pumping is now done electrically.

Plate 11. Curry Moor Pumping Station (The Somerset Rivers Drainage Board)

A large tract of land in Somerset has been mechanically drained for over a century, once with eight steam-driven pumping stations. Eastons made many units of this type for land drainage, for home and abroad, and the largely self-contained design assisted in avoiding damage when, as always, the land sank as it was drained. The engine frame, pump case, and well lining are of cast iron, the whole being bolted together into a single unit. This was made by Easton, Amos & Sons, London, in 1864, the cylinders being 20 in bore × 2 ft stroke, developing up to 150 hp at 48–50 rpm with steam at 60 psi. The use of parallel motion to guide the crosshead was usual in this design, with the condenser air pump, and boiler-feed pumps, driven from it. The centrifugal pump is at the bottom of the vertical shaft, the weight being taken by a thrust block in the semicircular casting above the smaller bevel wheel. The large bevel wheel has wooden teeth inserted into slots in the rim, held in place by flat steel strips at the back of the rim. This engine drained 3,800 acres for almost a century, and is now preserved in a neat brick house. Three other engines from the Somerset drainage systems are also preserved, at the Aller Moor Station near Burrow Bridge, each of which differs from the Curry Moor example.

Plate 12. Engine of PS *Leven* (Dumbarton Town Centre)

This was the first engine made by Robert Napier, who did so much for marine engineering upon the Clyde. Built in 1824, it embraces many of the features which were retained as long as side lever engines were built, i.e., late in the 1860s. Thus it has the round-backed 'D' slide valve, with the jet condenser in the middle above the lever centre, and the air pump between the condenser and the crank. Attractively plain throughout, the slide valve is driven by a slip eccentric by which, once the engine was set running in the required direction by hand operation of the slide valve, it continued to run in the right way. The single cylinder is about 30 in bore × 3 ft 6 in stroke, and it originally would use steam at about 2 to 4 psi, from a boiler which was little more than a rectangular tank, with internal furnaces and flue to the funnel. A classic example of the sound practice which was to make Scotland famous in engineering, it was made with the simplest equipment, and gave many years of service upon the River Clyde.

Plate 13. Engines of PS *Clyde* (Renfrew Ferry Landing)

The grasshopper type of side-lever engine was widely used for paddle-tug propulsion particularly upon the Clyde and Tyne. This is typical of the many that served on dock systems for general towing, and which continued to be made into the present century. In contrast to the engine of PS *Leven*, the beams are suspended at one end, with the drive to the crankshaft taken near to the cylinder, and the condensers are placed below the cylinders. The use of guides rather than parallel motion to guide the crosshead was a common feature of this design. It was customary to make the engines independent in this type, to give rapid manœuvring with an engineman to control each, but the engines had to be coupled together in a seaway by law. In *Clyde* the disconnection was by a sliding crank web, to allow the freedom to operate independently, or be coupled together. The fitting of link motion reversing gear was an unusual feature in this type of engine, but otherwise these are typical Clydeside design: plain, simple and reliable. (Photo: courtesy of John Butt.)

Plate 14. Engines of PS *Empress* (The Maritime Museum, Southampton)

These are probably the only surviving oscillating engines made by John Penn & Son of Greenwich, who did so much to develop the type, and they illustrate the very high standard of finish and design reached by the Thameside engineers in their heyday. These were made in 1879, and fitted to the hull built by Samuda & Co. at Millwall as PS *Empress*, for Cosens & Co., Weymouth, for their passenger services. The cylinders are 30 in bore × 2 ft 9 in stroke and, originally jet-condensing, used salt water in the boiler, which worked at 30 psi. The engines were preserved when the vessel was condemned about 1956, and given a very accomplished overhaul by the marine-engineering cadets of the Southampton College of Technology. They are exhibited in fine condition as they were at sea. Interesting features are the

Penns nuts, which have the washers beneath the heads formed solidly with the nuts themselves, and the fitting of link motion probably due to their late date, as many such engines were fitted with single slipping eccentrics. The original jet condenser was the chamber between the cylinders, with the air pump driven from the centre crank and the sea-water injection cock was in the space blanked off in front. They were converted to surface condensing about 1888.

Plate 15. Henwood Pumping Station (Ashford Waterworks, Kent)
The water-supply system was purchased by the council in 1882, when there was one engine only (that seen in the print), and this was followed by the other engine in 1885. Both were made by Thos. Horn of Westminster, and are a good type of small waterworks plant. The cylinders are about 8 in and 14 in bore × 1 ft 6 in and 2 ft 3 in strokes, with slide valves, and the pumps are three throw ram type in the wells. In the earlier engine all of the gearing has cast-iron teeth, but in the later the larger gear wheel has wooden teeth inserted in the rim, which avoided the noise made by all iron gears. There are several refinements in the later engine which show developments made in the years between their manufacture. Thus the earlier one has a cast-iron connecting rod, with forged straps for the upper bearings, whereas the later engine has a forged connecting rod, with a single top-end bearing in a jaw-end cast on the beam. They illustrate the high standards which were achieved in the nineteenth century even by small shops such as Horn's, many of which only lasted for the lifetime of the founder. Electric pumps are now in use, but the engines are preserved.

Plate 16. Morton Colliery Engine, Derbyshire (Leicester Civic Museum)
The shafts were sunk in the early 1860s, and this engine was supplied in 1865, to wind 3 tons 10 cwt of coal per wind from 750 ft deep, which it did for nearly a century until the colliery was closed in 1966. Made by A. Handyside & Co. of Derby, the cylinders are 30 in bore × 5 ft stroke, with slide valves driven by Stephenson's link motion worked from the centre of the connecting rods. The slide valves are unusual in that the steam is taken through a connection on the back of the valves chest and through the valves, which are simply hollow boxes, in contrast to the usual layout, where the steam is in the chest itself. The colliery produced 8,000 tons of coal per week in its heyday, and the original boilers, which were of the externally fired egg-ended type, were replaced by internally fired Lancashire boilers early in the present century. When the engine was built it was fitted with piston tail rods, but the Clay Cross Co. removed them from all of their engines since they were found to have very little value. The engine is now stored in the Leicester Museum, for re-erection later.

Plate 17. Fieldhouse Brickworks Engine (Tolson Museum, Huddersfield)
A very early example of horizontal winding engine, this wound clay from the pit at the Fieldhouse Brickworks for many years, after which

it hauled railway trucks in the works, to the early 1960s. The maker is unknown. It probably dates from the 1850s, and the drive has at some time been changed from the right- to the left-hand side. The cylinder is about 9 in bore × 2 ft stroke, and it is interesting for the long connecting rod, and the placing of the slide valve on the top of the cylinder, the simple block guide for the piston rod, and the open eccentric rod – all early engine features. When the brickworks was closed, the engine was presented by the owners, and then extremely well restored to its present state by Messrs Broadbents of Huddersfield. It is almost certainly the only engine of the type remaining.

Plate 18. Baggs' Brewery Engine, Kings Lynn (The Bridewell Museum, Norwich)

The largest engine in an attractive county museum, this engine worked at Baggs' Brewery, probably from the 1840s until the brewery was closed in 1930, when it was presented to the Museum. An attractive little engine, it does not appear ever to have had a condenser, and would develop 6–8 hp on steam at 60 psi. The cylinder is about 8 in bore × 1 ft 6 in stroke, and it was designed to take the drive from either side, simply by moving the crankshaft and bearing from one side to the other. Completely independent of the building, all of the parts are attached to the box bed. The curved brackets attached to the side of the fine, fluted centre column may have been added, but it is interesting that there is a similar arrangement on an engine in the Henry Ford museum in U.S.A. The parallel motion is of a very unusual type, and the brackets supporting the beam centre bearing and the radius rods, are most attractively curved.

Plate 19. Small Oscillating Engines (The Bridewell Museum, Norwich)

Two delightful examples of the simplest industrial design, and probably as small as any engines made for regular daily work, these two oscillating engines show several differences in design. The horizontal one, with a cylinder about 3 in bore × 4 in stroke, has the slide valve operated only by a linkage, but it has an eccentric to drive the boiler feed pump. Probably made in a country workshop, it is as simple as could be, yet it has the features of the larger oscillating designs. The vertical engine has a more sophisticated valve gear, with an eccentric to provide the movement, and a sector to allow for the oscillation of the cylinder in working. Another difference from the other engine is that the cylinder in this is suspended from the end, i.e., it is pendulous rather than oscillating. Each of these engines is a good example of a small working engine, and they show how, even in the smallest sizes, there was much individuality.

Plate 20.   Weaving Shed Engine (Near India Mill, Darwen, Lancs)

Preserved in the open air in the centre of Darwen, this is a typical medium-sized weaving-shed engine, which developed about 450 hp at 75 rpm, using steam at 120 psi. It is also equally typical of the design so long and successfully adopted by John and Edward Wood of Bolton, who adopted Corliss valves by 1870, and almost always fitted the inlet and exhaust valves together at the bottom of the cylinder. The print shows it to be a neat engine with an open appearance, and other Wood features are the placing of the steam stop valve beside the high-pressure cylinder-valve gear, and the simple design of the trip gear and governor. These were all features of their design good enough to be retained for many years until they closed in 1912, and which gave a highly economical performance. The cylinders are about 16 in and 32 in bore × 3 ft 6 in stroke, and together with one still at work in Yorkshire, and the large one under the care of the Industrial Steam Preservation Society, are all that remain of the large output of engines up to 2,500 hp made to this design.

Plate 21. White's Tannery Engine (The Bradford Industrial Museum, Yorks)

A good example of the small engines which were the mainstay of industry for many years, this single-cylinder slide-valve engine with a cylinder $15\frac{1}{4}$ in × 2 ft 6 in, was made by the local concern Carr, Foster of Bingley, about 1900. It powered Messrs J. White's tannery for nearly seventy years, and developed 80 hp at 90 rpm, when using steam at 100 psi, and exhausting to the works process heating system. The parts are fitted upon a single bed casting. The governor acted upon a separate cut-off valve on the main slide valve, and it drove the works machinery by a belt from the flywheel rim. A cylinder rebore in 1958 was probably the largest expenditure in its long life. It is probably the last surviving engine made by a general engineering concern which did much for the local mills. It is exhibited in the museum.

Plate 22. Courtaulds' Dee Mill Engine (Shaw, near Oldham, Lancs)

This is the last remaining horizontal mill engine made by Scott & Hodgson of Guide Bridge, and was installed to drive the Dee cotton-spinning mill in 1907. It is a twin tandem compound, with cylinders $18\frac{1}{2}$ in and 44 in bore × 5 ft stroke each side, and developed 1500 hp when running at 60 rpm on steam at 160 psi. The tiling of the engine house is notably complete, and the high quality indicates the consideration given to this at the time, but it was unusual to carry the tiling up in the window spaces, as most of the Lancashire engine rooms had large windows. It was a quiet and attractive engine, with Corliss valves for the high-pressure, and piston valves for the low-pressure cylinders. It is preserved at the mill, in the care of the Northern Mill Engines Society, by the courtesy of the owners. Visits are by permission of Messrs Courtaulds.

Plate 23. Carbolite Mill Engine (Bamford, Derbys)

This is a good example of the advanced thinking of the Lancashire engine builders. When continental drop-valve engines proved highly economical around the end of the nineteenth century, Petries of

Rochdale, and Musgraves of Bolton engaged Continental engineers to design such engines for them. Musgraves chose Mr Stegen from Switzerland, whose drop-piston valve engines proved very successful, and this is probably the last of about 40 such engines that he designed for them over some twenty years. It was installed by Messrs Olivers, in their cotton-doubling mill in Bamford, in 1907, and continued to drive the mill for some sixty years until it was closed. The new owners, Messrs Carbolite, kept the engine intact although they do not use it; it can be seen on Friday afternoons by permission. It developed 400 hp from the tandem cylinders of 16 in and 30 in bore × 2 ft 6 in stroke, and ran at 103 rpm, on steam at 160 psi. The site was originally a corn mill which was purchased because of the water power for the cotton mill, started at the end of the eighteenth century. The entire mill drives were rearranged in 1907, with a new engine house for the tandem engine, and conversion to rope drives from it.

Source References and Notes

Chapter One: Origins and Early Development

1. D. S. L. Cardwell: *Technology, Science and History*, 1972, p. 66.
2. See particularly J. B. Snell: *Mechanical Engineering – Railways*, 1971.
3. Von Guericke published an account of his experiments in *Experimenta nova Magdeburgica*, 1672. For a useful summary, see Cardwell, op. cit., p. 54.
4. H. W. Dickinson: *A Short History of the Steam Engine*, 1938 (Cass reprint with a new Introduction by A. E. Musson, 1963), p. 20, gives a description of Savery's patents.
5. R. L. Galloway: *Annals of Coalmining and the Coal Trade*, 1898, reprinted Newton Abbot, 1971, vol. 1, p. 198. Galloway reports an attempt to use a Savery engine in a flooded mine near Wednesbury, Staffordshire, but it failed.
6. A. E. Musson and Eric Robinson: *Science and Technology in the Industrial Revolution*, 1969, chapter XII – 'The Early Growth of Steam Power'. This important study is based on an article in the *Economic History Review*, vol. XI, Second Series, no. 3, 1959, by the same authors, but revisions and additions have been made to it.
7. Abraham Rees: *Cyclopaedia*, 1819 – the article on 'Steam Engine or Fire-Engine' is in vol. 34.
8. The best biographical study is L. T. C. Rolt: *Thomas Newcomen – The Pre-History of the Steam Engine*, 1963.
9. The *Transactions of the Newcomen Society* contain several valuable articles on early Newcomen engines. See in particular: T. E. Lones: 'The Site of Newcomen's Engine of 1712' (vol. 13, 1932–3); W. O. Henderson: 'Wolverhampton as the Site of the First Newcomen Engine' (vol. 26, 1947–9); and J. S. Allen: 'The 1712 and Other Newcomen Engines of the Earls of Dudley' (vol. 37, 1964–5) and 'Some Early Newcomen Engines and the Legal Disputes' (vol. 41, 1968–9).
10. J. T. Desaguliers: *A Course of Experimental Philosophy*, 1734–44.
11. See Rolt, op. cit., pp. 120–21, where the complete list is reproduced.
12. Rolt, op. cit., pp. 68–9, observes that the first Newcomen engine installed in the North of England was at the Gins pit in Whitehaven in 1715.
13. Joan Day: *Bristol Brass – A History of the Industry*, Newton Abbot, 1973, reproduces on p. 51 the sketch made by Reinhold Angerstein of the Warmley steam engine in 1754.

14. Rolt, op. cit., p. 89.
15. H. Kirke: 'Dr Clegg, Minister and Physician in the 17th and 18th
    Centuries', in: *Journal of the Derbyshire Archaeological Society*,
    vol. 35, 1913, and quoted by Rolt, op. cit., p. 90.
16. Rolt, op. cit., pp. 85–7. See also Mikulas Teich: 'Diffusion of
    Steam-, Water-, and Air-Power to and from Slovakia during the
    18th Century and the Problem of the Industrial Revolution', in:
    L'Acquisition des techniques par les pays non-initiateurs, Paris, 1973.
17. Isaac Bangs: 'New York in 1776', in: *Historical Magazine*, vol.
    4, Second Series, Dec. 1868, pp. 305–6, and quoted in Carroll
    W. Pursell Jr: *Early Stationary Steam Engines in America*,
    Washington D.C., 1969, pp. 7–9, to whom we are grateful for
    drawing our attention to this account.
18. *Stationary Steam Catalogue*, Science Museum Publication, 1925,
    p. 32.
19. The second cylinder acts as a condenser to the first, and was objected
    to by Watt for infringing his patent on this point.
20. H. W. Dickinson: *James Watt – Craftsman and Engineer*, Cam-
    bridge, 1935, p. 36. This was part of an account by Robert Hart,
    recorded many years after the event, in 1813.
21. Dickinson: *Short History*, p. 80.
22. Ibid., p. 83. See also Rex Wailes: *The English Windmill*, 1954,
    pp. 136–7, on the governor in windmills.
23. James Lord: *Capital and Steam Power, 1750–1800*, 1923, was one
    of the first scholars to use this material, although many have since
    done so. See, for instance, Eric Robinson and A. E. Musson: *James
    Watt and the Steam Revolution – a Documentary History*, 1969.
24. For an account of the Albion Mills, see John Mosse: 'The Albion
    Mills, 1784–1791' in: *Transactions of the Newcomen Society*, vol.
    40, 1967–8, pp. 47–60.
25. Lord, op. cit., pp. 172–3, gives a Table of 'Engines Erected out of
    England by Boulton & Watt from 1775–1800', showing a total of
    36 (8 in Wales, 21 in Scotland, 3 in Ireland, 2 in France, and 2 in
    Spain). But Lord's estimates elsewhere are curiously low: he gives
    a total of only 289 engines in England for the same period.

Chapter Two: Apotheosis

1. The Cruquius Engine has been the subject of several studies. For
   a useful summary, see Richard L. Hills: 'The Cruquius Engine,
   Heemstede, Holland' in: *Industrial Archaeology*, vol. 3, no. 1,
   Feb. 1966, pp. 8–15.
2. Sulzers, however, had the help of an outstanding British designer,
   C. E. L. Brown. See S. B. Saul: 'The Nature and Diffusion of
   Technology' in: A. J. Youngson (ed.), *Economic Development in the
   Long Run*, 1972, pp. 51–2.
3. The Corliss valve was patented by G. H. Corliss in the U.S.A. in
   1849, and the first in Europe was imported into Scotland in 1859.
   Corliss valves were being made by Douglas & Grant in Scotland by

1863, and almost simultaneously Hick of Bolton began manufacturing them.

4. Saul, op. cit., p. 50.
5. The point is made in J. Bronowski: *William Blake, 1757–1827*, 1944, p. 126. Bronowski, indeed, claims that Blake 'never went north of London'.
6. Sir Walter Scott: *Familiar Letters*, 1894, vol. 2, p. 78, and quoted in H. Perkin: *The Origins of Modern English Society 1780–1880*, 1969, pp. 178–9.
7. Samuel Butler: *Erewhon*, 1913 edn, p. 249. The satire first appeared in 1872.
8. For a sensitive treatment of the literary reaction to mechanization, see Herbert L. Sussman: *Victorians and the Machine – the Literary Response to Technology*, Cambridge, Mass., 1968. For a more extensive treatment of this whole field, see Francis D. Klingender: *Art and the Industrial Revolution*, edited and revised by Sir Arthur Elton, 1968.
9. Rees, op. cit., 1819.
10. John Farey: *Treatise on the Steam Engine – Historical, Practical and Descriptive*, 1827. Only one volume was published in the original edition of 1827, but when it was reprinted by David & Charles in 1971 a second volume was added, as Farey had intended, having been compiled from notes which were still in the course of preparation at the time of the author's death in 1851 and which had not been previously published.
11. Andrew Ure: *The Philosophy of Manufactures – or, An Exposition of the Scientific, Moral, and Commercial Economy of the Factory System of Great Britain*, 1835.
12. G. R. Porter: *The Progress of the Nation, in Its Various Social and Economical Relations, from the Beginning of the Nineteenth Century*, first published in serial form, 1836–43, and subsequently passing through many editions. This quotation is from p. 178 of the 'New Edition' of 1847.
13. Ibid., section ii, chapter ii, on 'Manufactures', p. 235. There is a curious statistical inconsistency between this and the previous reference, the increase in steam horse power in Manchester between 1800 and 1835 being more than fifty-fold on Porter's own figures.
14. *Quarterly Review*, vol. 79, Dec. 1846–March 1847, no. 157, p. 107.
15. John Bourne: *A Treatise on the Steam Engine*, 1846.
16. A. Toynbee: *Lectures on the Industrial Revolution in England*, 1884, reprinted Newton Abbot, 1969. The reference is to p. 90 in the reprinted edition.
17. For a perceptive treatment of the development of the science of thermodynamics, see Donald S. Cardwell: *From Watt to Clausius – The Rise of Thermodynamics in the Early Industrial Age*, 1971.

Chapter Three: Decline

1. See S. B. Saul: *The Myth of the Great Depression*, 1969, for a useful summary of scholarly discussion of this subject.
2. For a treatment of the rise of electricity generation and the problems involved, see R. H. Parsons: *The Early Days of the Power Station Industry*, 1940. Also P. Dunsheath: *A History of Electrical Engineering*, 1962; and T. K. Derry and Trevor I. Williams: *A Short History of Technology*, Oxford, 1960, p. 617.
3. This was von Kempelen's design – see Dickinson, *Short History*, pp. 187–9. Trevithick made somewhat similar experiments with a 'whirling engine' in 1815 – ibid., p. 190.
4. Pursell, op. cit., pp. 120–24, gives an account of American experience.
5. *The Engineer*, 1 Dec. 1899.
6. ibid., 6 July 1900.
7. ibid., 4 Jan. 1901.
8. R. Scott Burn (ed.): *The Steam Engine User, being practical descriptions and illustrations of the stationary steam engine in its various forms*, 1894, Introduction by the Editor, p. 2.
9. *Engineering*, 14 Sept. 1900.

Chapter Six: The Engine-Builders

1. These figures are from a list of Musgrave's engines compiled by employees of the firm, and now in the Watkins Collection.
2. There is an interesting account of this firm in Nancy Crathorne: *Tennant's Stalk*, 1973, pp. 131–2.
3. These figures are compiled from the annual reviews of shipbuilding and marine engineering which appeared in the columns of *Engineering*.
4. *Engineering*, 3 Jan. 1908.

Chapter Seven: The Steam Engine in Perspective

1. It is not possible to give precise figures for the number of Newcomen engines in the eighteenth century, but intensive local research in a few areas has enabled some reasonable estimates to be made, of which this figure of 300 engines by 1775 is one. It is probably a conservative estimate. J. R. Harris suggests the figure in his pioneering article – 'The Employment of Steam Power in the Eighteenth Century' in: *History*, vol. 52, no. 175, June 1967: 'To suggest that the true number of instances of the engine's employment is likely to be around 300 (for the period 1733 to 1781) seems moderation itself . . .', p. 144. Lord, op. cit., calculated a total of approximately 130 'old type engines' *at work* in 1775, but this did not allow for engines which had already gone out of commission, and as we have noticed elsewhere Lord seems to err on the side of understatement.
2. Musson and Robinson: *Science and Technology* . . ., pp. 393–426.
3. The colliery at Brora has been at work intermittently since the sixteenth century. It was the subject of a note in *Industrial Archaeology*,

vol. 6, no. 1, Feb. 1969, pp. 98–9 (although this did not mention the engine), at which time it was being run as a co-operative project by a small group of miners.

4. Dr Hills made these remarks in the course of a paper to the First International Conference on the Conservation of Industrial Monuments (FICCIM), held at Attingham Park, Shropshire, in June 1973. The Proceedings were published by the Ironbridge Gorge Museum Trust, 1975.

5. The reconstruction has been described in a paper to the Newcomen Society by Richard L. Hills, publication of which is pending. It is based on Barney's engraving of the 1712 engine.

Select Bibliography

The books listed here are either in print or available through public libraries. We have omitted early studies of steam power, some of which were of considerable distinction and significance, unless they have been reprinted recently. Also, we have kept references to articles in journals to a few samples, although the interested reader would be well advised to consult the *Transactions of the Newcomen Society* and the quarterly journal, *Industrial Archaeology*, for further information.

Allen, J. S. 'The 1712 and Other Newcomen Engines of the Earls of Dudley' – *Transactions of the Newcomen Society*, vol. 37, 1964–5.

Baker, W. A. *From Paddle Steamer to Nuclear Ship*, C. A. Watts, 1965.

Barton, D. B. *The Cornish Beam Engine*, Barton, Truro, 1965.

Bonnet, H. *The Saga of the Steam Plough*, David & Charles, Newton Abbot, 1971.

Buchanan, R. A. *Industrial Archaeology in Britain*, Pelican, 1972.

Cardwell, D. S. L. *From Watt to Clausius – The Rise of Thermodynamics in the Early Industrial Age*, Heinemann, 1971.

Steam Power in the Eighteenth Century, Sheed & Ward, 1963.

Technology, Science and History, Heinemann, 1972.

Clark, R. H. *The Development of the English Steam Wagon*, Goose, 1963.

Davidson, C. B. *Steam Road Vehicles – A Historical Review*, 1953 and 1970.

Derry, T. K., and Williams, T. I. *A Short History of Technology*, Oxford, 1960.

Dickinson, H. W. *A Short History of the Steam Engine*, 1938, Cass reprint, 1963.

James Watt – Craftsman and Engineer, Cambridge, 1935.

and Arthur Titley: *Richard Trevithick – The Engineer and the Man*, Cambridge, 1934.

Farey, J. *Treatise on the Steam Engine – Historical, Practical and Descriptive*, vol. 1, first ed, 1827, reprinted David & Charles, Newton Abbot, 1971; vol. 2 first published by David & Charles, 1971.

Fletcher, W. *Steam on Common Roads*, 1891, reprinted by David & Charles, Newton Abbot, 1971.

Galloway, R. L. *Annals of Coalmining and the Coal Trade*, 2 vols, 1898, reprinted David & Charles, Newton Abbot, 1971.

Guthrie, A. *A History of Marine Engineering*, Hutchinson, 1972.

Harris, J. R. 'The Employment of Steam Power in the Eighteenth Century' – *History*, vol. 52, no. 175, June 1967.

Harris, T. R. *Arthur Woolf – The Cornish Engineer*, Barton, Truro, 1970.

Hills, R. L. *Power in the Industrial Revolution*, Manchester, 1970.
'The Cruquius Engine, Heemstede, Holland' – *Industrial Archaeology*, vol. 3, no. 1, Feb. 1966.

Law, R. J. *The Steam Engine – A Short Introduction*, Science Museum, 1965.

Lord, J. *Capital and Steam Power, 1750–1800*, Westminster, 1923.

Musson, A. E., and Robinson, Eric. *Science and Technology in the Industrial Revolution*, Manchester, 1969.

Norris, W. *Modern Steam Wagons*, 1906, reprinted by David & Charles, Newton Abbot, 1971.

Parsons, R. H. *The Early Days of the Power Station Industry*, Cambridge, 1940.

Pursell, Carroll W., Jr. *Early Stationary Steam Engines in America*, Smithsonian Institution, Washington D.C., 1969.

Robinson, Eric, and Musson, A. E. *James Watt and the Steam Revolution*, Adams & Dart, 1969.

Rolt, L. T. C. *Thomas Newcomen – The Prehistory of the Steam Engine*, David & Charles, Newton Abbot, 1963.
Tools for the Job, Batsford, 1965.

Saul, S. B. 'The Nature and Diffusion of Technology' – Youngson, A. J. (ed.): *Economic Development in the Long Run*, Allen & Unwin, 1972.

Singer, C. *et al.*: *A History of Technology*, 5 vols., Oxford, 1954–8.

Smith, E. G. *A Short History of Marine Engineering*, Cambridge, 1938.

Spratt, H. P. *Marine Engineering* (descriptive catalogue of exhibits), 1952, reprinted 1970.
Merchant Steamers and Motorships (descriptive catalogue of exhibits), 1949, reprinted 1970.

Storer, J. D. *A Simple History of the Steam Engine*, John Baker, 1969.

Sussman, H. L. *Victorians and the Machine – the Literary Response to Technology*, Cambridge, Mass., 1968.

Thurston, R. H. *A History of the Growth of the Steam Engine*, 1879.

Tyler and Haining. *Ploughing by Steam*, Model and Allied Publications, 1970.

Watkins, G. *The Stationary Steam Engine*, David & Charles, Newton Abbot, 1968.
The Textile Mill Engine, vols. 1 & 2, David & Charles, Newton Abbot; vol. 1 – 1970, vol. 2 – 1971.

Index